MODERN CHEMICAL KINETICS

Selected Topics in Modern Chemistry

SERIES EDITORS

Professor Harry H. Sisler
University of Florida
Gainesville, Florida

Professor Calvin A. VanderWerf
Hope College
Holland, Michigan

Published

EYRING AND EYRING—*Modern Chemical Kinetics*
HILDEBRAND—*An Introduction to Molecular Kinetic Theory*
KIEFFER—*The Mole Concept in Chemistry*
MOELLER—*The Chemistry of the Lanthanides*
OVERMAN—*Basic Concepts of Nuclear Chemistry*
RYSCHKEWITSCH—*Chemical Bonding and the Geometry of Molecules*
SISLER—*Chemistry in Non-Aqueous Solvents*
SISLER—*Electronic Structure, Properties, and the Periodic Law*
VANDERWERF—*Acids, Bases, and the Chemistry of the Covalent Bond*

In Preparation

CHELDELIN AND NEWBURGH—*The Chemistry of Some Life Processes*
ROCHOW—*Organometallic Chemistry*

Series Editors' Statement

A distinguishing characteristic of modern chemical science is the extent to which it has been possible to ascertain the behavior of atoms, molecules, and ions during the course of a chemical reaction and to understand the various parameters which determine not only the products of a chemical reaction but the specific course which it follows. This most important field in which the rates and mechanisms of reactions are studied and which is known as chemical kinetics provides the subject for this new addition to SELECTED TOPICS IN MODERN CHEMISTRY.

Unlike most of the volumes in the series, this volume, because of the complexity of the subject matter treated, is directed chiefly toward upper class chemistry students rather than those in the earlier college years. We are indeed pleased to be able to present this volume from two distinguished authors whose contributions to research in chemical kinetics have so clearly established their pre-eminence in the field about which they have written.

Harry H. Sisler
Calvin A. VanderWerf

MODERN
CHEMICAL KINETICS

HENRY EYRING
and
EDWARD M. EYRING

Department of Chemistry
University of Utah
Salt Lake City, Utah

New York
REINHOLD PUBLISHING CORPORATION
Chapman & Hall, Ltd., London

PREFACE

The fundamental purpose of this book is to sketch for undergraduate chemistry students some of the important developments of the last three decades in the field of reaction rate chemistry. It is impossible for so short a book to provide a thorough survey of so large a field. Rather, it is hoped that at least a few readers will be infected by the typical reaction kineticist's enthusiasm for his subject and will delve deeper into the voluminous literature on modern chemical kinetics. It is also hoped that this book will provide useful insights for the professional as well as the tyro, in spite of the fact that the bulk of the information has appeared in print elsewhere.

After a brief introduction, the reader will find four chapters treating absolute rate theory and its experimental applications. The concluding chapter deals with one of the most exciting recent developments in the field of reaction kinetics—experimental studies of fast reactions in solution.

Equations and figures are numbered consecutively throughout a chapter. Where reference is made to an equation in a preceding chapter as, for example, Eq. 4.23 the first number is that of the chapter and the number following the period is that of the equation in the chapter. In several places the abbreviation Q. C. denotes the book, "Quantum Chemistry," by Henry Eyring, J. Walter, and G. E. Kimball, John Wiley & Sons, Inc., New York, 1944.

The Readings and References at the end of the chapters are, in fact, somewhat abbreviated bibliographies to the contents of the respective chapters.

We would like to thank the American Institute of Physics and McGraw-Hill Book Company for permission to reproduce Fig. 2.8 and John Wiley & Sons, Inc. for permission to reproduce Figs. 4.2 and 5.1.

We are grateful also to Mrs. Barbara Staker who drew the other figures in the text and to Misses Belva Barlow, Libbie Lyman, and Mehl Ree Draper for their careful assistance in preparing the manuscript.

The meticulous editing and proof reading by John Hart and other members of the Reinhold staff are greatly appreciated.

HENRY EYRING
EDWARD M. EYRING

January, 1963
Salt Lake City, Utah

CONTENTS

————————————

chapter one

ORIGIN OF THE ACTIVATED
STATE CONCEPT

ONE OF THE MOST remarkable phenomena that we observe daily is the process of growth in nonliving as well as living things. For instance, how does the elegant symmetry of a snowflake develop in the polluted atmosphere of a modern city? Evidently, the minute snow crystal surfaces have a much greater affinity for water molecules than for other molecules of comparable freezing points. The chemist routinely takes advantage of this property of crystal growth when he purifies a substance by recrystallizing it from a slowly cooling super-saturated solution. Crystal growth is certainly a striking example of nature's selectivity of reactants, but an even more spectacular instance of selectivity is the growth of long chains of amide-linked alpha amino acids, $\overset{\alpha}{NH_2}CHRCOOH$, to form the various proteins of the human body. Here, the choice of reactants is confined not simply to a select group of 20 alpha amino acids, but even these are unacceptable unless they are of the L-form (see Fig. 1.1). Even more remarkable is the fact that all living things on our planet share this prejudice against incorporating D-amino acids in their protein structures. The purpose of this book is to show how modern principles of reaction kinetics provide satisfying explanations for these and other intriguing chemical rate phenomena.

The modern era of chemical kinetics was ushered in by Wilhelmy's study of the inversion of cane sugar (sucrose) in 1850. Using a polarimeter, he followed the reaction

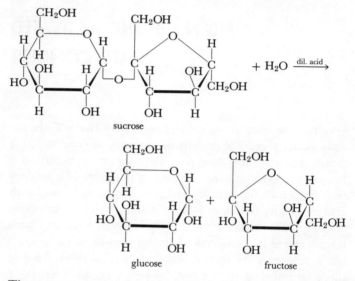

The sucrose rotates the plane of polarized light to the right (clockwise). However, as hydrolysis proceeds, the rotation shifts to the left because the fructose obtained rotates the plane of polarized light to the left more strongly than the glucose rotates it to the right. Wilhelmy noted that the concentration of sucrose decreases exponentially with time. This result may be expressed mathematically by the set of equations

$$-dc/dt = k_1 c \qquad\qquad 1.1$$

$$\ln c = k_1 t + \text{constant} \qquad\qquad 1.2$$

$$c = c_0 \text{ at } t = 0 \qquad\qquad 1.3$$

whence
$$c = c_0 e^{-k_1 t} \qquad\qquad 1.4$$

Here, c represents the concentration of sucrose at time t and k_1 is the "specific rate" or "rate constant" for the reaction. The expression *rate contant,* is misleading since k is actually a function of temperature and pressure. Thus Wilhelmy was the first to correctly formulate the kinetic law of a first order reaction. This reaction in aqueous solution is said to be first order, since the right hand side of the differential form of the rate expression contains the concentration of only one species raised to the first power. In general, the reaction order is not necessarily an integral or even positive number, since it is the sum of concentration exponents in the differential rate expression for an over-all reaction that may involve several discrete steps. The reaction order is not to be confused with the molecularity of a reaction which describes the mechanism of a discrete step in the over-all reaction. The molecularity will never be other than one, two, or three. The nitric acid

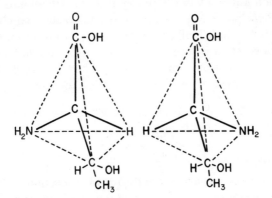

Fig. 1.1. L and D forms of the nutritionally essential alpha amino acid called threonine.

"catalyst" in Wilhelmy's experimental system makes the sucrose more reactive, but it is not depleted as the "inversion" or hydrolysis of the sucrose proceeds.

The inversion of sucrose is more complicated than Wilhelmy's elegant simplification would suggest. Denoting sucrose by S, we in fact have

$$S + H^+ \rightleftharpoons SH^+$$

$$SH^+ + H_2O \xrightarrow{\text{slow}} \text{glucose} + \text{fructose} + H^+$$

$$-d[S]/dt = k[SH^+][H_2O] = kK_c[S][H^+][H_2O]$$

Thus the c of Eq. 1.1 really represents the complex concentration of the substrate-catalyst rather than simply that of the sucrose. The absence of water from the rate expression is a consequence only of the fortuitous choice of the solvent: $[H_2O]$ experiences a negligible decrease when the reaction proceeds in aqueous solution. The inversion of sucrose under these conditions is thus more properly termed a "pseudo first-order" reaction.

The next important step in the development of modern reaction kinetics was the proposal by Guldberg and Waage of a Principle of Mass Action in reaction rates and chemical equilibria. Van't Hoff suggested that at equilibrium the net rate of reaction is zero, i.e., at equilibrium the forward and reverse rates of reaction are equal. Thus we can derive the familiar expression for the concentration equilibrium constant

$$[a][b]k = [c][d]k'$$

$$\frac{[c][d]}{[a][b]} = K_c = k/k'$$

1.5

where k is the specific rate of the forward reaction and k' that of the reverse reaction. In several scientific papers appearing between 1864 and 1879, Guldberg and Waage described and explained the effect of changing concentrations on the rates of simple reactions, such as the reversible combination of an alcohol with acetic acid to form an ester and water. Let us consider an even simpler case, the reaction

$$2NO + O_2 \rightarrow 2NO_2 \qquad 1.6$$

at high pressures occurring entirely in the gas phase (hence a homogeneous reaction). The rate of disappearance of NO is given by the product $k_3(NO)^2(O_2)$. In this particular case the exponents of the concentration terms in the rate expression are the stoichiometric coefficients of the reactants. Many interesting chemical reactions are complex in the sense that they involve more than one discrete step. For such reactions a simple one to one correspondence between stoichiometric coefficients and exponents in the differential equation for the rate of the over-all reaction does not exist. To this extent the concept of Mass Action does not have the generality of application to reaction rates that it does have to equilibria. In 1877, van't Hoff independently enunciated the Principle of Mass Action, applied it to heterogeneous systems, and subsequently did much to interest his fellow scientists in the quantitative study of reaction kinetics.

In 1889, Arrhenius published his conclusion that molecules must get into an activated state before they become reactive. He had noted that the influence of temperature on the rate of acid-catalyzed hydrolysis of sucrose (Fig. 1.2) is too great to be explained either by an increase in kinetic energy of all the molecules or by an increased dissociation of the acid catalyst. Arrhenius also had van't Hoff's result for the temperature dependence of the concentration equilibrium constant K_c. The van't Hoff equation may be written as

$$\frac{d \ln K_c}{dT} = \frac{\Delta E}{RT^2} \qquad 1.7$$

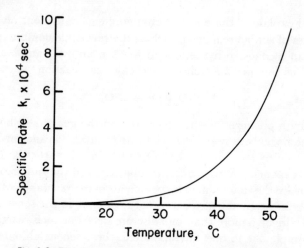

Fig. 1.2. Temperature dependence of the rate of acid catalyzed hydrolysis of sucrose. $[H^+] = 0.19$ M, 5% sugar solution (Moelwyn-Hughes, 1934).

where the increase of energy ΔE is equal to the heat of reaction at constant volume. It follows from Eqs. (1.5) and (1.7) that

$$\frac{d \ln k}{dT} - \frac{d \ln k'}{dT} = \frac{\Delta E}{RT^2} \qquad 1.8$$

Van't Hoff suggested that Eq. (1.8) could be split into two equations

$$\frac{d \ln k}{dT} = \frac{E}{RT^2} + A \quad \text{and} \quad \frac{d \ln k'}{dT} = \frac{E'}{RT^2} + A \qquad 1.9$$

where $\Delta E = E - E'$ and A is a constant. Equation 1.9 fits experimental results best with A taken to be zero. Arrhenius therefore proposed the use of

$$\frac{d \ln k}{dT} = \frac{E_A}{RT^2} \qquad 1.10$$

This relation is commonly called the Arrhenius equation. Arrhenius further assumed that E_A is a constant (only approximately correct) and obtained on integrating Eq. 1.10.

$$\ln k = -\frac{E_A}{RT} + \text{constant} \quad \text{or} \quad k = Ae^{-E_A/RT} \qquad 1.11$$

Oddly enough Eq. 1.11 is not properly applicable to the sucrose inversion data that suggested it. In the 0° to 40° C temperature range the activation energy E_A decreases precipitously with rising temperature, at a rate of about -223 cal/deg, in the H^+ catalyzed system (Moelwyn-Hughes, 1947). The classic results of Bodenstein (1894–1898) for the gaseous reactions

$$H_2 + I_2 \rightleftharpoons 2HI$$

(commonly considered to be four center second order processes (Porter, 1956)) provide a more satisfactory application though here also there is a definite temperature coefficient of E_A, about $+35$ cal/deg for the backward reaction in the temperature range 283° to 508° C. As we see from Fig. 1.3, Eq. 1.11 gives a good fit of Bodenstein's experimental results over a fairly extended temperature range. The achievement for which Arrhenius is justly famous is not this arithmetic agreement but rather its interpretation. He suggested that in a reacting system an equilibrium exists between ordinary and "active" molecules, and only the latter are rich enough energetically to undergo reaction. The apparent activation energy E_A in Eqs. 1.10 and 1.11 is the difference between the average energy of active molecules and the average energy of all the molecules. Tolman (1927) showed that the integrated form of the Arrhenius equation will always be invalid unless these two averages have precisely the same temperature dependence.

The Arrhenius concept of active molecules immediately

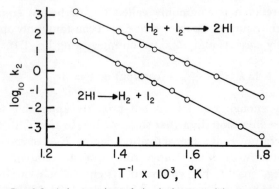

Fig. 1.3. Arrhenius plots of the hydrogen iodide reactions (Bodenstein).

suggests the explanation for the rule of thumb that the rate of a reaction is approximately doubled by a 10 degree rise in temperature. (This generalization is true of reactions having intermediate values of E_A. For example, in the case of the reaction $H_2(g) + I_2(g) \rightarrow 2HI(g)$ we have $E_A \cong 42.4$ kcal at $25°$ C and 1 atm.) Translational, rotational and vibrational energy of the reacting molecules will all contribute to E_A. The energy distribution function will have the shape shown schematically in Fig. 1.4. Only the long high energy tail of the distribution function will experience a significant increase in area with a modest rise in temperature. However, it is precisely this area from which the active molecules responsible for reaction come. The difference between the two curves in Fig. 1.4 has been exaggerated in the interests of clarity; a ten degree temperature rise would effect a much less dramatic, though still important, increase in the area of the foot of the curve.

This is a good time to call attention to the fact that there are many chemical reactions that do not have this temperature dependence. The adsorption of nitrogen gas on a clean

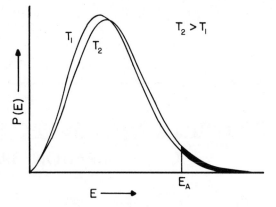

Fig. 1.4. Dependence of molecular energy upon absolute temperature.

tungsten surface or the enzyme-catalyzed hydrolysis of the acetylcholine ion in the human body are examples of non-Arrhenius kinetics.

Readings and References

Frost, A. A., "Effect of Concentration on Reaction Rate and Equilibrium," *J. Chem. Ed.*, **18**, 272 (1941).

Frost, A. A., and Pearson, R. G., "Kinetics and Mechanism," 2nd Ed., Chaps. 1, 2, John Wiley & Sons, Inc., New York, 1961.

Leicester, H. M., and Klickstein, H. S., "A Source Book in Chemistry," pp. 396–400, 468–471, McGraw-Hill Book Co., New York, 1952.

Johnson, F. H., Eyring, H., and Polissar, M. J., "The Kinetic Basis of Molecular Biology," Chap. 1, John Wiley & Sons, Inc., New York, 1954.

Moelwyn-Hughes, E. A., "The Kinetics of Reactions in Solution," Chap. 2, Oxford University Press, London, 1947.

Porter, G., "Kinetics of Reactions in Gases," *Ann. Rev. Phys. Chem.*, **7**, H. Eyring, ed. (Annual Reviews, Inc., Palo Alto, 1956).

Tolman, R. C., "Statistical Mechanics with Applications to Physics and Chemistry," Chap. 20, Chemical Catalog Co., Inc., New York, 1927.

chapter two

POTENTIAL ENERGY SURFACES IN CONFIGURATION SPACE

Introduction

What developments were necessary before the Arrhenius concept of passive and active molecules could lead to an *a priori* calculation of the specific rate of a chemical reaction? Let us begin answering this question by considering the hypothetical chemical reaction

$$XY + Z \underset{R_b}{\overset{R_a}{\rightleftharpoons}} XYZ^{\ddagger} \underset{R_d}{\overset{R_c}{\rightleftharpoons}} X + YZ \qquad 2.1$$

The species $XYZ^{\ddagger}$ called the activated complex is the intermediate species resulting from "collision" of XY and Z. Let us assume that $XYZ^{\ddagger}$ has the linear structure $X \ldots Y \ldots Z$ in which the old bond between X and Y (not necessarily atoms) is partially broken while the new bond between Y and Z is still only partially formed. $XYZ^{\ddagger}$ does not represent the "active" molecules of Arrhenius. His active or energized species are rather the few reactant molecules XY and Z having sufficient energy to get into the "transition state" or activated complex condition, but not necessarily the spatial configuration corresponding to the transition state. The existence of a high concentration of the intermediate $XYZ^{\ddagger}$ compared to the concentration of reactants XY and Z is precluded by the higher potential energy of the $XYZ^{\ddagger}$ "molecule." A short, qualitative digression on the nature of potential energy surfaces will be helpful at this point.

Ignoring for the moment the nature of the forces of interaction, we recall that the potential energy of a system of two or more interacting bodies is a function of their relative positions. Thus, in the case of the diatomic hydrogen molecule, we have the ground electronic state potential energy curve of Fig. 2.1. Here the resultant, F, of attractive and repulsive

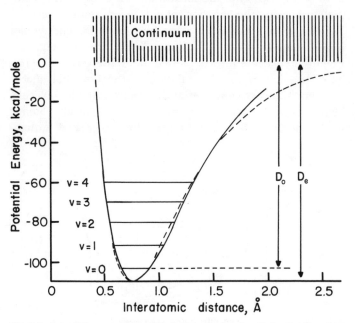

Fig. 2.1. Potential energy curve of H_2 in its ground state with the first few vibrational levels denoted by the horizontal lines. The full curve is drawn from Rydberg's spectroscopic data. The broken curve is a Morse curve.

forces favors an equilibrium internuclear separation r of 0.75Å for which F vanishes. The potential energy at this distance is a minimum with the zero of potential energy taken as that for infinite interatomic separation. In the more complicated case of an n-atomic molecule, an $(f + 1)$ dimensional space is required in which to plot potential energy as a function of configuration of the nuclei. Here f is the number of independent variables required to completely specify relative positions of all n nuclei in the molecule. Let us again assume that $XYZ^{\ddagger}$ has a linear configuration and that X, Y, and Z of reaction (1) above represent atoms. Then f will be 2 since only two internuclear distances are required to completely specify the location of all three atoms. Hence a 3-dimensional space is adequate for a potential energy plot in configuration space of the linear XYZ system (see Fig. 2.2). Potential energy is always plotted along the vertical coordinate. Implicit in this formulation of the potential energy problem is the assumption that the electrons in the molecule, being much lighter, move much faster than the atomic nuclei; hence, as Born and Oppenheimer suggested, a quan-

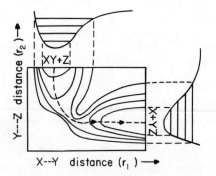

Fig. 2.2. Typical potential energy surface for the reaction $XY + Z \rightarrow X + YZ$.

tum mechanical calculation of electronic energy can be made with the nuclei considered to be stationary. An earlier and more familiar variant of the Born-Oppenheimer approximation is the Franck-Condon principle according to which "vertical transitions" occur between potential energy surfaces corresponding to the different electronic states of molecules.

Now let us return to the reaction between XY and Z. Distance is measured along the lowest energy path from reactants to products, and the dashed line in Fig. 2.2, is called the reaction coordinate. It turns out that if potential energy is plotted along the vertical z-axis of a Cartesian coordinate system and the internuclear distances $X \dots Y$ (denoted r_1) and $Y \dots Z$ (denoted r_2) are plotted along the x and y axes respectively, the position on the surface corresponding to the activated complex $XYZ^{\ddagger}$ will generally be a saddle point between the lower energy regions of the stable XY and YZ molecules. We must emphasize that the activated state can be defined as having a particular energy, but in addition it must have the particular geometric configuration of the transition state. Since the potential energy surface is concave downward along the reaction coordinate at the transition state, $XYZ^{\ddagger}$ has no stability in either direction along this coordinate. However, $XYZ^{\ddagger}$ is stable at right angles to the reaction coordinate and vibrates in this direction.

The primary objective of this chapter is to show how to map a potential surface in configuration space. To do this we need to outline at least the rudiments of wave mechanics.

The London Equation

In principle, the potential surface for a chemical reaction can be determined by quantum mechanical calculations. In practice, the computational difficulties are horrendous for even the comparatively simple H_3 system that involves only 3 electrons. For this reason a semiempirical surface for H_3

devised by H. Eyring and M. Polanyi is still widely used. This semiempirical surface and a modified version proposed recently by Sato are both based on the London equation to be discussed below. Following a qualitative outline of its derivation, we will show how the London equation is applied to the kinetics of the H_3 system. We choose this case not simply because H_3 is conveniently depicted in a 3-dimensional potential energy-configuration space, but also because the most convincing tests, though by no means the most fruitful applications, of the absolute rate theory have been made with the systems H_3, H_2D, HD_2, etc.

The calculation of the lowest energy of a simple system of electrons and atomic nuclei is a primary objective of quantum mechanics. The lowest energy state is interesting because it corresponds to the most stable and, in general, the most heavily populated state of a system of electrons and nuclei. The instantaneous position and velocity of an electron are impossible to predict simultaneously with a precision greater than that given by the Heisenberg Uncertainty Principle

$$\Delta p \Delta q \approx h \qquad 2.2$$

where Δp and Δq are the respective uncertainties in momentum and position and Planck's constant $h = 6.62 \times 10^{-27}$ erg-sec. Electrons, unlike the customary bodies of classical mechanics, have such small masses that the uncertainties in their momentum and position are appreciable compared to the absolute values of these quantities. It is therefore necessary to resort to the use of wave mechanics with its associated wave functions or "eigenfunctions ψ" to describe the behavior of small particles such as the electrons and the atomic nuclei. This is completely analogous to our description in physical optics of light quanta, the particles of light, as waves. The probability P of finding an electron in the volume element $d\tau$ is proportional to the product of ψ, its complex conjugate

ψ^* and the volume element $d\tau$. ψ^* is readily obtained by replacing i by $-i$ wherever it occurs in ψ. The product $\psi\psi^*$ must be used rather than ψ^2 in order that the probability P should never have an imaginary value. Figs. 2.3 and 2.4 depict the relationship between $\psi\psi^*\ d\tau$ and $r^2\psi\psi^*\ dr$, the radial distribution function or probability that the electron lies in a spherical shell of thickness dr concentric with the nucleus and a distance r from the nucleus.

The classical Hamiltonian of a particle

$$H = \frac{1}{2m}(p_x{}^2 + p_y{}^2 + p_z{}^2) + V(x,y,z) \qquad 2.3$$

is an expression for the sum of the kinetic energy T and potential energy V of the system in terms of the coordinates and momenta of the individual particles. According to one of the fundamental postulates of quantum mechanics, the Hamiltonian of n electrons and n fixed nuclei can be converted to the operator

$$\mathbf{H} = -\frac{h^2}{8\pi^2 m}\sum_i \nabla_i{}^2 - \sum_{A_i}\frac{z_A e^2}{r_{A_i}} + \sum_{AB}\frac{z_A z_B e^2}{r_{AB}} + \sum_{ij}\frac{e^2}{r_{ij}} \qquad 2.4$$

where e is the charge on one electron, m is the mass of an electron, r_{A_i} is the distance of the ith electron from the Ath nucleus, r_{AB} is the distance between any pair of nuclei A and B with charges z_A and z_B, r_{ij} is the distance between the ith and the jth electrons, $\nabla_i{}^2 = \dfrac{\partial^2}{\partial x^2} + \dfrac{\partial^2}{\partial y^2} + \dfrac{\partial^2}{\partial z^2}$ and h is Planck's constant. The masses of the nuclei are comparatively large so the relative kinetic energy of the nuclei is at first neglected. If the operator $\mathbf{H}$ is allowed to operate on an eigenfunction ψ of this system, the corresponding energy E of the system is given by the Schrödinger equation

$$\mathbf{H}\psi = E\psi \qquad 2.5$$

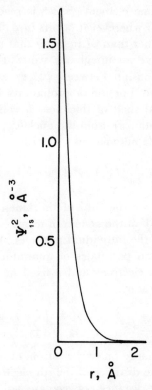

Fig. 2.3. Plot of $\psi_{1s}\psi_{1s}^*$ for the hydrogen atoms versus the distance r of the electron from the nucleus.

$$\psi_{1s} = \left(\frac{1}{4\pi}\right)^{1/2} 2\left(\frac{Z}{a_0}\right)^{3/2} e^{-\frac{Zr}{a_0}}$$

where Z is the nuclear charge and $a_0 = 0.529$ Å. The subscript 1s denotes the principal quantum number $n = 1$, and the azimuthal quantum number $l = 0$. Since $l = 0$, the eigenfunction is spherically symmetrical about the nucleus.

where E is said to be an eigenstate of the Hamiltonian operator. An equivalent form of this equation for a single particle is

$$\frac{\partial^2 \psi}{\partial x^2} + \frac{\partial^2 \psi}{\partial y^2} + \frac{\partial^2 \psi}{\partial z^2} + \frac{8\pi^2 m}{h^2}(E - V)\psi = 0 \qquad 2.6$$

Like all differential equations, Eqs. 2.5 or 2.6 has an infinite number of solutions for any given form of the potential energy V. Physically meaningful solutions are obtained by

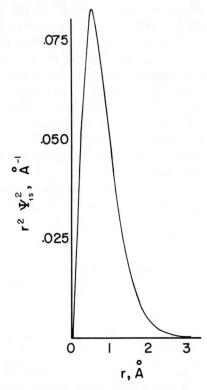

Fig. 2.4. The radial distribution function $r^2\psi\psi^*$ for the 1s orbital of the hydrogen atom.

imposing on ψ and its first derivatives with respect to x, y and z the restriction that they be everywhere single valued, finite and continuous. Thus we generally start out with a known form of the potential energy V plus the Schrödinger equation and obtain values of the energy E corresponding to various forms of the wave function ψ. The problem of selecting the ψ that yields a lowest value of E for the system is resolved by either one of two trial and error approximation methods: the variation method or the perturbation method. Using the variation method, one never calculates an energy less than the true lowest energy of the system. By incorporating enough independent parameters into the assumed eigenfunction of the ground state of the system and then varying these parameters until a minimum energy is obtained, the difference between the resultant calculated energy and the true energy can be made smaller than any preassigned value. Unfortunately, the integrals in the expression for E obtained by this method are extremely difficult to evaluate even for the comparatively simple H_3 system and the simplest possible eigenfunctions.

By making several rather serious approximations,* London derived the following equation for the lowest energy state of a four electron system with respect to the separated electrons:

$$E = (1 + k)^{-1}(Q - \{\tfrac{1}{2}[(\alpha - \beta)^2 + (\beta - \gamma)^2 + (\gamma - \alpha)^2]\}^{1/2}) \qquad 2.7$$

In this expression k is the sum of the squares of the electron orbital overlap integral and Q represents a sum of Coulombic interaction integrals for the various electron pairs (see Fig. 2.5)

---

* The Born-Oppenheimer approximation is made; the electronic orbitals used are not designed to treat mutual electronic repulsions accurately and hence assign the electrons too high or too low a probability of being close together; the vast majority of reactions are presumed to proceed adiabatically, i.e., on a single potential surface with no contributions made by reactants in excited electronic states; multiple exchange integrals are omitted from consideration.

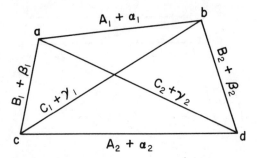

Fig. 2.5. Coulombic and exchange energies for a system of four electrons.

$$Q = A_1 + A_2 + B_1 + B_2 + C_1 + C_2 \qquad 2.8$$

While α and β frequently denote electron spin in quantum mechanics, in the present context they, with γ, represent instead sums of "exchange integrals," i.e., $\alpha = \alpha_1 + \alpha_2$ where α_1 is an integral arising from the quantum mechanical (nonCoulombic) interaction of electrons a and b of Fig. 2.5. In considering all possible arrangements of electrons about nuclei it is frequently necessary to exchange the orbital co-ordinates of two electrons. This purely formal manipulation gives rise to this so-called exchange binding energy that is also familiar as the resonance energy of organic chemistry. The analogue of Eq. 2.7 for three electrons is readily obtained by imagining the d atom with its electron in Fig. 2.5 to be removed. Thus the quantities A_2, B_2, C_2, α_2, β_2 and γ_2 disappear. Writing A, B, C, α, β and γ for A_1, B_1, C_1, α_1, β_1 and γ_1 respectively as in Fig. 2.6, we then have for the London equation for 3 electrons Eq. 2.8 where the symbols now represent different quantities.

An important step in the chain of events leading up to an *a priori* calculation of H_3 kinetics was the development by Heilter, London, and Sugiura, in 1927, of equations for the

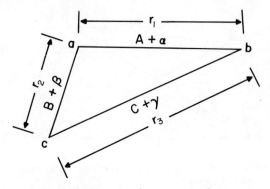

Fig. 2.6. Coulombic and exchange energies for a system of three electrons.

energy of the singlet (ground) and triplet (first excited) electronic states of the H_2 molecule. With this information one can calculate the separate Coulombic and exchange energies of any of the possible diatomic molecules in the H_3 structure as a function of internuclear separation. The ratio of Coulombic to total binding energy for H_2 is shown in Fig. 2.7. The calculated equilibrium internuclear separation and minimum in potential energy differ from experiment by about 8 and 32 per cent respectively. Errors of this magnitude are not unexpected since the Heilter-London-Sugiura equations are only approximate.

The Semiempirical Method

In 1931, H. Eyring and M. Polanyi circumvented these difficulties with a procedure known as the "semiempirical method." First they assembled from spectroscopic measurements the following information regarding a given diatomic molecule: D_e, the heat of dissociation plus the zero point energy; r_0, the equilibrium interatomic distance of the normal molecule; and ω_0, the equilibrium vibration frequency. Then they plotted a Morse curve (like that of Fig. 2.1) from the equation

$$E = D_e[e^{-2a(r-r_0)} - 2e^{-a(r-r_0)}] \qquad 2.9$$

where $a = 0.1227\omega_0(\mu/D_0)^{1/2}$, μ is the reduced mass of the molecule, and D_0 is the heat of dissociation of the molecule. They next assumed on the basis of Fig. 2.7 that to a sufficiently good approximation over the important range of internuclear distances the Coulombic energy is a constant fraction

$$\rho = \frac{\text{Coulombic energy}}{\text{total binding energy}} \qquad 2.10$$

of the total binding energy given by the Morse curve for various internuclear distances. Thus it is possible in the case

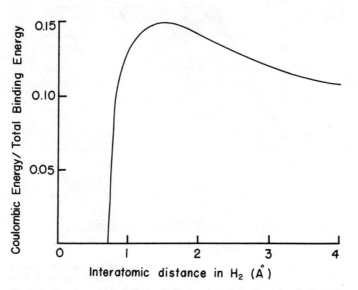

Fig. 2.7. The proportion of Coulombic energy to total energy for the H_2 molecule as a function of interatomic distance.

of the H_3 activated complex to calculate individual terms in all three sums $A + \alpha$, $B + \beta$ and $C + \gamma$ for any values of r_1, r_2 and r_3 where these latter denote the internuclear distances in Fig. 2.6. The square of the overlap integral k in Eq. 2.7 is assumed to be negligibly small, and values of E are calculated for a large number of internuclear distances. Fig. 2.8 is a plot of the resulting potential surface for the H_3 system. By choosing the coordinate system in which r_1 and r_2 make an angle of sixty rather than the usual ninety degrees, the expression for the relative kinetic energy of the three atoms takes the form of a single particle moving on the potential surface. Thus the trajectory of the particle on this skewed surface would represent the course of reaction and a calcula-

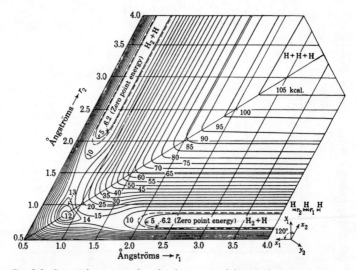

Fig. 2.8. Potential energy surface for the system of three hydrogen atoms based on an assumed 14 per cent Coulombic energy, i.e., $\rho = 0.14$ [Eyring, H., Gershinowitz, H., and Sun, C. E., J. Chem. Phys., **3**, 785 (1935)].

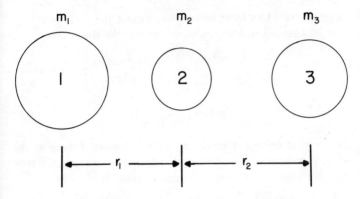

Fig. 2.9. System of three atoms lying on a straight line.

tion of its motion yields the corresponding vibrational frequencies of the H_3 system.

The internal kinetic energy of a system of three interacting atoms on a line (see Fig. 2.9) relative to its center of mass is

$$T = \frac{1}{2M}[m_1(m_2 + m_3)\dot{r}_1^2 + 2m_1m_3\dot{r}_1\dot{r}_2 + m_3(m_1 + m_2)\dot{r}_2^2] \quad 2.11$$

where $M = m_1 + m_2 + m_3$. By plotting r_1 and r_2 as skew axes at an angle of θ with respect to each other and by changing the scale of distance along the r_2 axis, it is possible to have the kinetic energy, T, take the form for a particle of mass m moving in the x, y, plane. In accord with this plan, let $r_1 = x - y \tan \theta$ and $r_2 = cy \sec \theta$. In this figure x and y are rectangular axes and c is a reduction factor. Inserting these values of r_1 and r_2 in T, we obtain

$$T = \frac{1}{2M}[m_1(m_2 + m_3)(\dot{x} - \dot{y} \tan \theta)^2 + 2m_1m_3(\dot{x} - \dot{y} \tan \theta)(c\dot{y} \sec \theta)$$

$$+ m_3(m_1 + m_2)c^2\dot{y}^2 \sec^2 \theta] \quad 2.12$$

Taking θ and c to be constant, we impose the condition that the cross-term involving xy must vanish. We then have

$$(2\dot{x}\dot{y}\tan\theta)m_1(m_2 + m_3) = 2m_1m_3\dot{x}\dot{y}c\sec\theta \qquad 2.13$$

or

$$\sin\theta = \left(\frac{m_3}{m_2 + m_3}\right)c \qquad 2.14$$

The second necessary condition for the system of three atoms to be representable by a particle moving on a surface is that the coefficients of $\dot{x}^2$ and $\dot{y}^2$ must be equal or

$$m_1(m_2 + m_3) = m_1(m_2 + m_3)\tan^2\theta - 2m_1m_3\tan\theta\sec\theta$$
$$+ m_3(m_1 + m_2)c^2\sec^2\theta \qquad 2.15$$

Substituting 2.14 in 2.15 and using trigonometric identities, we find that

$$\sin\theta = \left[\frac{m_1m_3}{(m_2 + m_3)(m_1 + m_2)}\right]^{1/2} \qquad 2.16$$

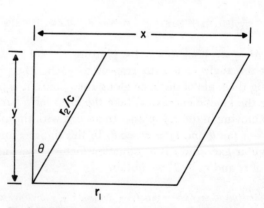

Fig. 2.10. Construction of a "diagonalized" potential energy coordinate system.

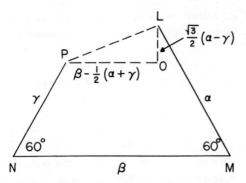

Fig. 2.11. Graphical determination of the contribution made by exchange energy integrals to the energy E given by the London equation.

Thus c modifies the scale of the sloping coordinate and θ skews the coordinate axes as in Fig. 2.10. We now have for the internal kinetic energy T of the system the desired relation

$$T = \tfrac{1}{2}m\dot{x}^2 + \tfrac{1}{2}m\dot{y}^2 \qquad 2.17$$

where $m = m_1(m_2 + m_3)M^{-1}$.

Once the integrals A, B, C, α, β and γ have been estimated by the semiempirical method, the London equation E can be rapidly evaluated by a graphical construction. Let us choose the lines LM, MN and NP of Fig. 2.11 so that they are equal in length to the numerical values of α, β and γ respectively. Simple trigonometric considerations lead us to

$$OL = \alpha \sin 60° - \gamma \sin 60°$$

$$PO = \beta - \alpha \cos 60° - \gamma \cos 60°$$

$$(PL)^2 = \alpha^2 + \beta^2 + \gamma^2 - \alpha\gamma - \alpha\beta - \gamma\beta \qquad 2.18$$

$$= \{\tfrac{1}{2}[(\alpha - \beta)^2 + (\beta - \gamma)^2 + (\gamma - \alpha)^2]\}^{1/2}$$

This last expression is, of course, the exchange energy contribution to the energy E of the London equation. This construction is valid for nonlinear as well as linear spatial configurations of the activated complex.

Equation 2.18 is particularly interesting since it provides a readily understandable argument for the linear configuration of the activated complex $H_3^{\ddagger}$. Let us consider the London equation for three electrons and Eq. 2.18 in conjunction with Figs. 2.6 and 2.11. We seek the lowest and consequently the most probable path over the saddle on the potential surface. The highest point on this optimum reaction path will correspond to the activated complex. Thus we want PL of Fig. 2.11 to have the largest possible value consistent with given values of α and β. γ must therefore be as small as possible and r_3 must be a maximum, or $r_3 = r_1 + r_2$, which corresponds to a linear configuration. Bending vibrations of the linear activated complex create small transitory angles in the complex. These bending vibrational frequencies are readily calculated using the potential energy of bending and the known kinetic energy expression for bending. The bending frequencies as well as the stretching frequencies of the activated complex enter into the expression for the rate of reaction in a manner to be developed later in this book.

The Potential Basin Near the Transition State

The semiempirical method has been criticized for the shallow depression at the top of the H_3 potential barrier (Fig. 2.8). This depression arises from the approximation that $\rho = 0.14$ is a constant over all configuration space. Since the quantum mechanical justification for this assumption is questionable, a recent semiempirical surface due to Sato that lacks this basin has enjoyed a certain vogue. Sato has used k, the sum of the squares of the overlap integral, in Eq. 2.7 as his empirical parameter rather than ρ with the result that in his calculations the latter varies considerably with internuclear distance though not necessarily in the same way as in Fig. 2.7. The price paid by Sato for the elimination of the basin is to get the barrier too thin as shown by excessively large tunnel effects. Figure 2.7 suggests a better way of obtaining a barrier of the correct height and with appropriate curvatures. We see in Fig. 2.7 that ρ is a strong function of internuclear separation at short distances of approach. Although the Heitler-London-Sugiura equations are certainly only qualitatively correct, they are a reasonably reliable justification for the following procedure. The Coulombic and exchange terms are calculated from the Morse curve for hydrogen using a value of ρ 1.4 times the value plotted in Fig. 2.7. The value 1.4 is chosen to give agreement with the observed activation energy. In Fig. 2.12, the resulting profile along the reaction path is compared with that obtained by Sato. The semiempirical surface obtained by the above

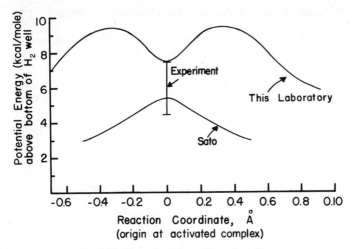

Fig. 2.12. Theoretical H_3 reaction path profiles.

procedure is in better accord with experiment than any other so far obtained.

Readings and References

Coolidge, A. S., and James, H. M., "The Approximation Involved in Calculations of Atomic Interaction and Activation Energies," *J. Chem. Phys.*, **2**, 811 (1934).

Coulson, C. A., "Valence," 2nd ed., chap. 5, Oxford University Press, London, 1961.

Eyring, H., and Polanyi, M., "Uber einfache Gasreaktionen," *Z. Physik. Chem.*, **12B**, 279 (1931).

Glasstone, S., Laidler, K. J., and Eyring, H., "The Theory of Rate Processes," chaps. 2, 3, McGraw-Hill Book Co., New York, 1941.

Hirschfelder, J., Eyring, H., and Rosen, N., "I. Calculation of Energy of H_3 Molecule," *J. Chem. Phys.*, **4**, 121 (1936).

London, F., "Quantenmechanische Deutung des Vorgangs der Aktivierung," Z. Elektrochem., **35**, 552 (1929).

Sato, S., "On a New Method of Drawing the Potential Energy Surface," and "Potential Energy Surface of the System of Three Atoms," *J. Chem. Phys.*, **23**, 592, 2465 (1955).

Shavitt, I., "A Calculation of the Rates of the Ortho-Para Conversions and Isotope Exchanges in Hydrogen," *J. Chem. Phys.*, **31**, 1359 (1959).

Weston, R. E., Jr., "H_3 Activated Complex and the Rate of Reaction of Hydrogen Atoms with Hydrogen Molecules," *J. Chem. Phys.*, **31**, 892 (1959).

chapter three

STATISTICAL MECHANICAL BASIS
OF RATE THEORY

Derivation of the Boltzman Probability Relationship

We require an answer to the following question: if the absolute temperature is T, what is the chance of finding a particular molecule, or group of molecules, in some precisely specified energy state? An atom can move in the three directions x, y and z with three independent velocities. Thus each atom is said to have three degrees of freedom. Each degree of freedom can take up energy in discrete amounts specified by an appropriate quantum number, and the energy for a system is the sum of the energies for the individual degrees of freedom.

Let us now consider a system A and represent the probability of its being in the ith state by P_i. This probability will depend on the temperature and the nature of A but not on what kind of a box A is enclosed in. Let us choose this container, i.e. our system B, so that our probability calculation is made as simple as possible. We will make system B out of $S/3$ solid atoms of such soft material that the vibration frequency, ν, is vanishingly small. The $S/3$ atoms have

$3(S/3) = S$ degrees of freedom and each degree of freedom can take up energy in integral multiples of h.

We next postulate that any unique, allowed way of distributing the total energy, E, in this composite system A plus B has the same probability as any other unique, allowed distribution. The important question then is, what is the probability that system A has the energy, ϵ_i, distributed in system A in some unique, allowed way? This specification allows the remaining energy $(E - \epsilon_i)$ to be distributed in all possible allowed ways in system B. An amount of energy $E - \epsilon_i$ provides $\dfrac{E - \epsilon_i}{h\nu} \equiv n_i$ quanta to distribute among the S oscillators of system B. This distribution can be made in N_i ways where

$$N_i = \frac{(n_i + S - 1)!}{n_i!(S - 1)!} \qquad 3.1$$

This expression for N_i may be understood as follows. Let us represent the n_i quanta by n_i circles and the S oscillators by S crosses. Then a possible way of distributing nine quanta to five oscillators is $(00X)(000X)(0X)(00X)(0X)$ where the circles inside a particular pair of parentheses represent quanta assigned to the oscillator which lies on their immediate right. So long as one cross is kept on the extreme right the remaining $(n_i + S - 1)$ quanta plus oscillators can be arranged in $(n_i + S - 1)!$ ways, each of which seemingly represents an acceptable arrangement. However, since the n_i quanta are indistinguishable, this number is too large by the factor $n_i!$. There is a further overcount of $(S - 1)!$ owing to the fact that any permutation of the $(S - 1)$ parenthetical quantities (leaving out the one to the extreme right) represents the same assignment of quanta to oscillators. Thus N_i of Eq. 3.1 gives correctly the number of ways of distributing

n_i quanta among S oscillators. The probability of system A having the energy ϵ_i in a unique way is then

$$P_i = \frac{N_i}{\sum\limits_i N_i} \qquad\qquad 3.2$$

where $\sum\limits_i N_i$ is the sum of all possible ways of distributing the energy.

Under most conditions of interest S may be supposed very large, i.e., in the neighborhood of Avogadro's number, while $n_i \gg S$, since by making our box of very soft material we have chosen $h\nu$ vanishingly small. Further for all the terms which make appreciable contributions to the denominator of Eq. 3.2 $\epsilon_i \ll E$, since system A will usually be a single molecule or at most a small group of molecules. Under these circumstances the expression for N_i can be simplified as follows

$$N_i = \frac{(n_i + S - 1)!}{n_i!\,(S - 1)!} = \frac{1}{(S - 1)!} \prod_{r=1}^{s} (n_i + S - r)$$

$$= \frac{1}{(S - 1)!} \prod_{r=1}^{s} \frac{E - \epsilon_i + h\nu(S - r)}{h\nu}$$

$$= \frac{1}{(S - 1)!} \left(\frac{E}{h\nu}\right)^S \left(1 - \frac{\epsilon_i}{E} + \frac{h\nu}{E}(\overline{S - r})\right)^S$$

$$\equiv \frac{1}{(S - 1)!} \left(\frac{E}{h\nu}\right)^S \left(1 - \frac{\epsilon_i}{S\gamma} + g\right)^S$$

$$\approx \frac{1}{(S - 1)!} \left(\frac{E}{h\nu}\right)^S \left(1 - \frac{\epsilon_i}{S\gamma}\right)^S = \frac{1}{(S - 1)!} \left(\frac{E}{h\nu}\right)^S e^{-\frac{\epsilon_i}{\gamma}} \qquad 3.3$$

In Eq. 3.3 γ symbolizes the average energy of an oscillator. Also $\quad g = \dfrac{\epsilon_i}{S\gamma} - \dfrac{\epsilon_i}{S\gamma + \epsilon_i} + \dfrac{h\nu}{E}(\overline{S - r})$. Hence we have

$g \ll \dfrac{\epsilon_i}{S\gamma}$ so that g can be neglected. The relationship $\left(1 - \dfrac{\epsilon_i}{S\gamma}\right)^S = e^{-\frac{\epsilon_i}{\gamma}}$ is correct. Using the binomial theorem and MacLaurin's expansion for an exponential, we have

$$\left(1 - \frac{\epsilon_i}{S\gamma}\right)^S$$

$$= 1 - \frac{S\epsilon_i}{S\gamma} + \frac{S(S-1)}{2}\left(\frac{\epsilon_i}{S\gamma}\right)^2 - \frac{S(S-1)(S-2)}{3!}\left(\frac{\epsilon_i}{S\gamma}\right)^3 + \cdots$$

$$\approx 1 - \frac{\epsilon_i}{\gamma} + \frac{1}{2!}\left(\frac{\epsilon_i}{\gamma}\right)^2 - \frac{1}{3!}\left(\frac{\epsilon_i}{\gamma}\right)^3 + \cdots = e^{-\frac{\epsilon_i}{\gamma}}$$

Substitution of the value N_i of Eq. 3.3 in Eq. 3.2 yields

$$P_i = \frac{e^{-\frac{\epsilon_i}{\gamma}}}{\sum\limits_i e^{-\frac{\epsilon_i}{\gamma}}} \qquad\qquad 3.4$$

Dulong and Petit noted that the heat capacity of a mole of metal, i.e., of $3 \times 6.02 \times 10^{23}$ oscillators in the classical temperature range is 6 calories per degree. For our very soft metal this heat capacity holds down to absolute zero so that the average energy, γ, of our oscillator in ergs is

$$\gamma = \frac{6T4.18 \times 10^7}{3 \times 6.02 \times 10^{23}} = 1.39 \times 10^{-16}T = kT \qquad\qquad 3.5$$

A more careful evaluation of k gives 1.3803×10^{-16} ergs/deg. We now rewrite Eq. 3.4 using the value for the average energy of our classical oscillator $\gamma = kT$ and obtain

$$P_i = \frac{e^{-\frac{\epsilon_i}{kT}}}{\sum\limits_i e^{-\frac{\epsilon_i}{kT}}} \qquad\qquad 3.6$$

The expression $\sum_i e^{-\frac{\epsilon_i}{kT}}$ is known as the partition function for system A and is of fundamental importance in thermodynamics and in reaction kinetics as we shall soon see.

From Eq. 3.6 it follows that at equilibrium the ratio of the number of molecules n_i in state i to the number, n_j, in state j is given by

$$\frac{n_i}{n_j} = \frac{\exp(-\epsilon_i/kT)}{\exp(-\epsilon_j/kT)} \qquad 3.7$$

We now define the activity, λ, by the equation

$$\lambda = \frac{n_i}{\exp(-\epsilon_i/kT)} = \frac{n_j}{\exp(-\epsilon_j/kT)}$$

$$= \frac{n_i + n_j}{\exp(-\epsilon_i/kT) + \exp(-\epsilon_j/kT)} \qquad 3.8$$

The last equality is justified as follows:

$$n_i = n_j \frac{\exp(-\epsilon_i/kT)}{\exp(-\epsilon_j/kT)} \qquad 3.9$$

adding n_j to both sides gives

$$n_i + n_j = n_j \frac{[\exp(-\epsilon_i/kT)]}{\exp(-\epsilon_j/kT)} + n_j$$

$$= n_j \frac{[\exp(-\epsilon_i/kT) + \exp(-\epsilon_j/kT)]}{\exp(-\epsilon_j/kT)} \qquad 3.10$$

Hence

$$\frac{n_i + n_j}{\exp(-\epsilon_i/kT) + \exp(-\epsilon_j/kT)} = \frac{n_j}{\exp(-\epsilon_j/kT)} = \lambda \qquad 3.11$$

Clearly this summation procedure may be extended to as many states as one pleases.

Statistical Thermodynamics

From the first and second laws of thermodynamics we can write the well known relationship

$$TdS = dE + dW \qquad 3.12$$

for any reversible process. This simply states that the heat, TdS, absorbed by a system in a reversible process is equal to the increase in energy of the system plus the work done by the system. T, S and E are the temperature, entropy and energy of the system, respectively. These are all properties of the system while W is the work done by the system. The Helmholtz free energy, A, is defined as

$$A = E - TS \qquad 3.13$$

Thus A is likewise a property of the system, since it is defined in terms of properties.

If Eq. 3.13 is differentiated and from the result Eq. 3.12 is subtracted, one obtains

$$dA = -SdT - dW \qquad 3.14$$

Eq. 3.14 shows that at constant temperature the decrease in Helmholtz free energy, A, measures the work done by the system. This is why the Helmholtz free energy is an interesting property. When the work is done only against an external pressure, Eq. 3.14 becomes

$$dA = -SdT - pdV \qquad 3.15$$

Since A is a property, one can write

$$dA = \left(\frac{\partial A}{\partial T}\right)_V dT + \left(\frac{\partial A}{\partial V}\right)_T dV \qquad 3.16$$

From a comparison of Eqs. 3.15 and 3.16 it follows that

$$\left(\frac{\partial A}{\partial T}\right)_V = -S \qquad 3.17$$

and

$$\left(\frac{\partial A}{\partial V}\right)_T = -p \qquad 3.18$$

Substituting Eq. 3.17 in Eq. 3.13, one sees that

$$E = -T^2 \frac{\partial (A/T)}{\partial T} \qquad 3.19$$

The average energy of a system is given by the probability, P_i, of being in a state multiplied by the corresponding energy, ϵ_i, of the state. Thus

$$E = \sum_i P_i \epsilon_i = \frac{\sum_i \epsilon_i e^{-\frac{\epsilon_i}{kT}}}{\sum_i e^{-\frac{\epsilon_i}{kT}}} \equiv kT^2 \frac{\partial \ln}{\partial T} \sum_i e^{-\frac{\epsilon_i}{kT}} \qquad 3.20$$

Equating the thermodynamic value for E, Eq. 3.19, to the statistical mechanical expression for the same quantity in Eq. 3.20 yields the equation

$$-T^2 \frac{\partial A/T}{\partial T} = kT^2 \frac{\partial \ln}{\partial T} \sum_i e^{-\frac{\epsilon_i}{kT}} \qquad 3.21$$

Integrating Eq. 3.21 gives

$$A/T = -k \ln \sum_i e^{-\frac{\epsilon_i}{kT}} - C \qquad 3.22$$

Here C is independent of T but may depend on V. Since more than one state with the same energy may occur, it is convenient to recognize this degeneracy explicitly. Accordingly we write

$$\sum_i e^{-\frac{\epsilon_i}{kT}} \equiv \sum_{j=1}^{\infty} \omega_j e^{-\frac{\epsilon_j}{kT}} \underset{T \to 0}{\approx} \omega_1 e^{-\frac{\epsilon_1}{kT}} \qquad 3.23$$

Here ω_j, the degeneracy, is the number of states having the energy ϵ_j. ω_1 and ϵ_1 are the degeneracy and energy of the lowest state, respectively. Thus as T approaches zero Eq. 3.22 becomes

$$A = E - TS = -kT \ln \omega_1 + \epsilon_1 - CT \qquad 3.24$$
$$T \to 0$$

At absolute zero one must make the identification $E = \epsilon_1$ and also $S = k \ln \omega_1 + C$. In accordance with the third law the entropy, S, is zero for stable systems, and since $k \ln \omega_1$ and C must both be positive they must each be separately equal to zero if the third law is to hold.

Thus the third law requires that $\omega_1 = 1$ and $C = 0$. This leaves us with the powerful result

$$A = -kT \ln \sum_i e^{-\frac{\epsilon_i}{kT}} \qquad 3.25$$

Now if the energy levels and their volume dependence are known this gives A as a function of V and T and all thermodynamic properties can be calculated from such an expression for A.

Equilibrium Constants

Consider, for example, the following equilibrium

$$N_2 + 3H_2 \rightleftharpoons 2NH_3 \qquad 3.26$$

In a volume, V, containing nitrogen, hydrogen and ammonia the number, n_i, of molecules of each kind is necessarily proportional to the sum of the probabilities of their being in the corresponding available states, i.e. proportional to the corresponding partition function. The subscripts 1, 2 and 3 will be used to designate quantities referring to nitrogen, hydrogen and ammonia, respectively.

Thus we have

$$\frac{n_3{}^2}{n_1 n_2{}^3} = \frac{\sum_j e^{-\frac{(\epsilon_j + E_0)}{kT}}}{\sum_i e^{-\frac{\epsilon_i}{kT}}} = e^{-\frac{E_0}{kT}} \frac{\sum_j e^{-\frac{\epsilon_j}{kT}}}{\sum_i e^{-\frac{\epsilon_i}{kT}}} \qquad 3.27$$

Here $n_3{}^2$ is the number of ways a pair of ammonia molecules can be chosen as required by Eq. 3.26 and similarly $n_2{}^3$ is equal to the required number of sets of three hydrogen molecules. Strictly we should write $n_3(n_3 - 1)$ instead of $n_3{}^2$ because a molecule cannot be counted twice for a pair, but since n_3 is large, this makes no difference.

As indicated in Fig. 3.1, E_0 is the heat of reaction at absolute zero. Eq. 3.27 leads to the following expression for the equilibrium constants, K_c, in terms of the concentrations of molecules per c.c.

$$K_c = \left(\frac{n_3}{V}\right)^2 \Big/ \left(\frac{n_1}{V}\right)\left(\frac{n_2}{V}\right)^3 = \frac{e^{-\frac{E_0}{kT}} \sum_j e^{-\frac{\epsilon_j}{kT}} \Big/ V^2}{\sum_i e^{-\frac{\epsilon_i}{kT}} \Big/ V^4} \qquad 3.28$$

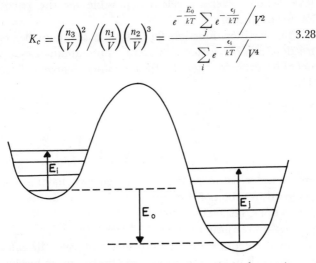

Fig. 3.1. Initial and final energy states in the synthesis of ammonia from nitrogen and hydrogen.

In order to proceed further we require explicit expressions for the partition function of our system.

Molecular Partition Function and Equilibrium Constants

As one example consider the partition function for the nitrogen molecule, N_2. Since the molecule contains two atoms, it has six degrees of freedom. Three of these are translations of the center of gravity, two are rotations, and one is a vibration. The total energy of a molecule is the sum of six energies, one for each degree of freedom. Thus we have

$$\epsilon_i = \epsilon_a{}^{I} + \epsilon_b{}^{II} + \epsilon_c{}^{III} + \epsilon_d{}^{IV} + \epsilon_e{}^{V} + \epsilon_f{}^{VI} \qquad 3.29$$

Here $\epsilon_a{}^{I}$ signifies the energy of level a of the first degree of freedom. For each energy, ϵ, the roman numeral used as a superscript indicates the degree of freedom while the letter used as a subscript is the quantum number of the occupied level where several levels are possible for the particular degree of freedom.

The partition function for a system of many degrees of freedom can be written to a useful approximation as a product of partition functions for the individual degrees of freedom. Thus

$$\sum_i e^{-\frac{\epsilon_i}{kT}} = \sum_a e^{-\frac{\epsilon_a{}^{I}}{kT}} \sum_b e^{-\frac{\epsilon_b{}^{II}}{kT}} \sum_c e^{-\frac{\epsilon_c{}^{III}}{kT}}$$

$$\sum_d e^{-\frac{\epsilon_d{}^{IV}}{kT}} \sum_e e^{-\frac{\epsilon_e{}^{V}}{kT}} \sum_f e^{-\frac{\epsilon_f{}^{IV}}{kT}} \qquad 3.30$$

We consider as an example, nitrogen gas, having mass m, enclosed in a box of dimensions l_1, l_2 and l_3 in the x, y and z directions, respectively.

For the translational degree of freedom in the x direction we must calculate the allowed energy levels. To calculate energy levels in general one requires the quantum mechanical solutions of the appropriate Schrödinger wave equations. In the case of translational energies it suffices to use the Wilson-Sommerfeld extension of the Bohr quantization rule for the levels in the hydrogen atom. This is:

$$n_1 h = \oint p \, dq = m\dot{x}l_1 + (-m\dot{x})(-l_1) = 2m\dot{x}l_1 \qquad 3.31$$

The equation states that the integral of the particle's momentum, p, times distance, dq, integrated over a cycle or round trip for the particle in this degree of freedom must equal Planck's constant, h, times an integer, n_1, for the allowed states.

Solving Eq. 3.31 for the velocity, $\dot{x}$, yields

$$\dot{x} = \frac{n_1 h}{2 l_1 m} \qquad 3.32$$

The allowed translational energy levels are accordingly

$$E_{n_1} = \tfrac{1}{2}m\dot{x}^2 = \frac{n_1^2 h^2}{8 l_1^2 m} \qquad 3.33$$

The corresponding translational partition function, f_1, is therefore

$$f_1 = \sum_{n_1=1}^{\infty} e^{-\frac{n_1^2 h^2}{8 l_1^2 mkT}} = \int_0^\infty e^{-\frac{n^2 h^2}{8 l_1^2 mkT}} \, dn_1 = \frac{(2\pi mkT)^{1/2}}{h} l_1 \qquad 3.34$$

with similar expressions for the y and z directions. Hence, the partition function for the three translational degrees of freedom, f_t, is the simple product

$$f_t = \frac{(2\pi mkT)^{3/2}}{h^3} l_1 l_2 l_3 \equiv \frac{(2\pi mkT)^{3/2} V}{h^3} \qquad 3.35$$

Here $V = l_1 l_2 l_3$ is the volume of the container.

The rotational energy of a linear molecule like nitrogen is

$$E_J = \frac{J(J+1)h^2}{8\pi^2 I} \qquad 3.36$$

This result follows from either quantum mechanics or spectroscopy (see Q.C.* p. 74).

Here the quantum number J takes integral values from 0 to infinity and I, the moment of inertia, has the value

$$I = \frac{m_1 m_2}{m_1 + m_2} r^2 \qquad 3.37$$

where r is the distance between the two atoms of masses m_1 and m_2, respectively. Each energy state is $2J + 1$ fold degenerate. Consequently the partition function, f_{2r}, for the two rotational degrees of freedom of the unsymmetrical rigid rotator is

$$f_{2r} = \sum_{J=0}^{\infty} (2J + 1) e^{-\frac{J(J+1)h^2}{8\pi^2 IkT}} \approx \int_{J=0}^{\infty} (2J + 1) e^{-\frac{J(J+1)h^2}{8\pi^2 IkT}} \, dJ \qquad 3.38$$

If we make the substitution $x = J + \frac{1}{2}$ then

$$f_{2r} = \int_{x=\frac{1}{2}}^{\infty} 2x e^{-\frac{(x^2 - \frac{1}{4})h^2}{8\pi^2 IkT}} \, dx = \frac{8\pi^2 IkT}{h^2} \qquad 3.39$$

For a symmetrical linear molecule in accord with quantum mechanics and spectroscopy only the levels corresponding to J odd or to J even are populated so that the partition function, being a sum over states, is cut in two. In general, therefore,

$$f_{2r} = \frac{8\pi^2 IkT}{\sigma h^2} \qquad 3.40$$

where the symmetry number, σ, is unity for unsymmetrical molecules and two if the molecules are symmetrical.

For a harmonic oscillator (see Q.C. p. 77) we find the

---

* In several places the abbreviation Q.C. denotes the book "Quantum Chemistry" by H. Eyring, J. Walter, and G. E. Kimball, John Wiley & Sons, Inc., New York, 1944.

allowed energy levels are given by the formula

$$E = (n + \tfrac{1}{2})h\nu \qquad 3.41$$

where n takes integral values from zero to infinity. Thus the vibrational partition function is

$$f'_v = \sum_{n=0}^{\infty} e^{-\frac{(n+\frac{1}{2})h\nu}{kT}} = \frac{e^{-\frac{h\nu}{2kT}}}{1 - e^{-\frac{h\nu}{kT}}}$$

$$\equiv \frac{1}{e^{\frac{h\nu}{2kT}} - e^{-\frac{h\nu}{2kT}}} = \frac{1}{2}\left[\sin h\left(\frac{h\nu}{2kT}\right)\right]^{-1} \qquad 3.42$$

This follows since $\displaystyle\sum_{n=0}^{\infty} x^{n+1/2} = \frac{x^{1/2}}{1-x}$ which is Eq. 3.42 where $x = e^{-h\nu/kT}$. Alternatively, it is equally satisfactory to base the vibrational partition function on the lowest allowed energy state which is at an energy $\tfrac{1}{2}h\nu$. In this case we have

$$E = nh\nu \qquad 3.43$$

and for the vibrational partition function we have

$$f_v = \frac{1}{1 - \epsilon^{-h\nu/kT}} \qquad 3.44$$

Nonlinear polyatomic molecules have three rotational degrees of freedom. By a procedure analogous to that for the two dimensional rotator the three dimensional rotational partition function, f_{3r}, is found to be

$$f_{3r} = \frac{8\pi^2(8\pi^3 ABC)^{1/2}(kT)^{3/2}}{\sigma h^3} \qquad 3.45$$

Here A, B and C are the three principal moments of inertia of a nonlinear molecule and σ is the symmetry number, i.e., the number of indistinguishable ways of orienting the rigid molecule. Thus $\sigma = 12$ for a hexagonal molecule such as benzene and also for a regular tetrahedral molecule such as methane and $\sigma = 2$ for an isosceles triangle such as water.

The partition function, f, for nitrogen with its six degrees of freedom is therefore

$$f_1 = \frac{(2\pi m_1 kT)^{3/2} V}{h^3} \frac{8\pi^2 I_1 kT}{2h^2} \frac{1}{1 - e^{-h\nu_1/kT}} \qquad 3.46$$

Finally, substituting the appropriate partition functions in the expression for an equilibrium constant in Eq. 3.28 gives

$$K_c = \frac{c_3^2}{c_1 c_2^3} = \frac{F_3^2}{F_1 F_2^3} e^{-E_0/kT} \qquad 3.47$$

The arbitrariness in including or omitting the half quanta from the vibrational partition function is apparent only. Equilibrium constants and specific reaction rate constants involve energy differences between the initial and final state and between the initial and the activated state, respectively. The same value for these differences is used no matter which standard states are chosen for the vibrational partition functions. Here the partition function per unit volume, F_1, of nitrogen is defined by the equation

$$F_1 = \frac{f_1}{V} \qquad 3.48$$

where f_1 is defined by Eq. 3.46. F_2, the corresponding partition function for hydrogen, is the same as F_1 except that the subscripts one are changed to two while for $F_3 = f_3/V$ for the ammonia molecule, we have

$$F_3 = \frac{(2\pi m_3 kT)^{3/2}}{h^3} \frac{8\pi^2 (8\pi^3 A_3 B_3 C_3)^{1/2} (kT)^{3/2}}{3h^3} \prod_{i=1}^{6} \frac{1}{1 - e^{-h\nu_i/kT}} \qquad 3.49$$

The ammonia molecule is a regular pyramid with nitrogen at the apex and so is a three dimensional rotator. Since there are three translational degrees of freedom it follows that the remaining six out of the total twelve degrees of freedom are vibrations. It should now be possible for the reader to write the equilibrium constant for any gaseous reaction. Where reactions involve molecules in the liquid or solid state appropriate changes in their partition functions can be made.

Activities

It is convenient at this point to redefine the activity, λ_i, of the ith molecule as

$$\lambda_i = \frac{n_i}{f_i'} = \frac{c_i}{F_i'} \qquad 3.50$$

See Eq. 3.11.

The primes in Eq. 3.50 are to remind us to take the same zero of energy for the partition functions of both reactants and products. It will be convenient to take as the reference energy level the lowest level of the reactants. Thus for nitrogen and hydrogen our definition yields $f_i' = f_i$ while for ammonia f_3' is defined by the equation

$$f_3' = f_3 e^{-E_0/2kT} \qquad 3.51$$

Here E_0 is the energy of reaction at absolute zero. Introducing activities into the expression for the equilibrium constant, Eq. 3.47 yields

$$\lambda_3{}^2 = \lambda_1 \lambda_2{}^3 \qquad 3.52$$

Thus at equilibrium the product of the activities of the reactants is equal to the product of the activities of the products for any reaction. This equation is equally applicable where all or a part of the reactants or products are solids or liquids. Consider for example the equilibrium between carbon dioxide, lime and limestone.

$$CaCO_3 = CaO + CO_2 \qquad 3.53$$

As before, we write for the standard equilibrium equation involving the activities of reactants and products

$$\lambda_1 = \lambda_2 \lambda_3 \qquad 3.54$$

Here the subscripts 1, 2 and 3 are assigned to the three constitutents in the order in which they appear in Eq. 3.53. Writing out the explicit expressions for activities in Eq. 3.54 yields

$$\prod_{i=1}^{15}\left(1 - e^{-\frac{h\nu_i}{kT}}\right) = \prod_{j=1}^{6}\left(1 - e^{-\frac{h\nu_j}{kT}}\right)\frac{n_3}{V}\left(\frac{(2\pi m_3 kT)^{3/2}}{h^3}\frac{8\pi^2 I_3 kT}{2h^2}\right)^{-1}$$
$$\prod_{l=1}^{4}\left(1 - e^{-\frac{h\nu_l}{kT}}\right)e^{\frac{E_0}{RT}} \quad 3.55$$

We can, of course, replace n_3/V, the concentration of CO_2 in Eq. 3.55 by its partial pressure using the equation

$$p_3/kT = n_3/V \qquad 3.56$$

The interesting point is that since condensed systems do not change their volumes appreciably with pressure it follows that λ_1 and λ_2 each have the value unity (for one molecule) divided by the partition function for a single molecule. These partition functions are products of vibrational partition functions, one for each degree of freedom. The exponent E_0/RT may be written with an R or a k depending on whether E_0, the energy of reaction at absolute zero, is for moles or for molecules reacting.

We now develop the theory of rates of elementary reactions.

Elementary Reaction Rates

In the first chapter it was shown that chemically stable systems are represented by valleys or basins lying on multidimensional potential surfaces and that a chemical reaction corresponds to the passage over or through the barriers separating such valleys or basins. For the rate, r, of an elementary reaction involving a single distinctly slowest step with negligible back reaction, we can write

$$r = \sum_j c_j^{\ddagger} k_j^{\ddagger} = \sum_j \lambda_j^{\ddagger} F_j^* k_j = \lambda_1 \lambda_2 \cdots \sum_j F_j^* k_j^{\ddagger}$$

$$= \frac{c_1}{F_1} \frac{c_2}{F_2} \cdots \sum_j F_j^* k_j^{\ddagger} \quad 3.57$$

The first summation in Eq. 3.57 states that in each state, j, there is a concentration, $c_j^{\ddagger}$, of activated complexes which decompose at a rate $k_j^{\ddagger}$ and that the total rate of reaction is a sum of contributions from all such states. By replacing $c_j^{\ddagger}$ by $\lambda_j^{\ddagger} F_j^*$, which is the product of the absolute activity of the activated complex by its partition function at constant volume in accord with Eq. 3.50, the second expression for the rate is obtained. The third expression makes use of Eq. 3.52 and equates the activity of the jth state, λ_j, to the product of the activities of the reactants with which it is in equilibrium. The fourth expression replaces the activities of reactants by the corresponding ratio of concentrations and partition functions in accord with Eq. 3.50.

Consider Fig. 3.2. The equilibrium concentration in the nth level at the top of the barrier is $c_n^{\ddagger}$ of which half of the systems at equilibrium are moving from left to right, in the direction of reaction, with a velocity

$$\dot{x}_n = \frac{nh}{2\delta m^{\ddagger}} \quad 3.58$$

(see Eq. 3.32). The rate at which systems in the nth state pass through the length δ is then

$$\frac{\dot{x}_n}{\delta} = \frac{nh}{2\delta^2 m^{\ddagger}} \quad 3.59$$

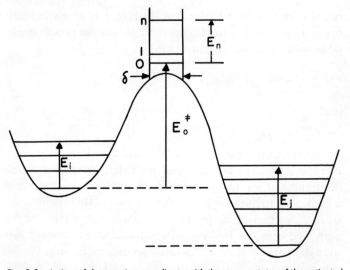

Fig. 3.2. A view of the reaction coordinate with the energy states of the activated complex at the top of the potential energy barrier denoted by the quantum numbers 0, 1, . . . n.

Even for systems that have traversed the barrier there is a chance that they will be reflected and not go onto reaction. Let us represent by the transmission coefficient, κ_{lmn}, the actual number of transitions successfully crossing the barrier under the conditions of the experiment divided by the equilibrium number if all crossings were successful. Here the subscript, n, specifies the quantum number for the one degree of freedom along the reaction coordinate while l signifies all the other quantum numbers of the initial state and m all the quantum numbers of the final state which should be specified to uniquely determine the initial and final state of the reacting systems. It will be convenient here to define an average transmission coefficient κ_n for the nth state $\kappa_n = \bar{\kappa}_{lmn}$ where $\bar{\kappa}_{lmn}$ is the sum over transmission coefficients to all final states m averaged over all initial states l for a given quantum number n along the reaction coordinate. Accordingly we write

$$F_j^* \equiv e^{-\frac{E_0^{\ddagger}}{kT}} \, F^{\ddagger} e^{-\frac{n^2 h^2}{8\delta^2 m^{\ddagger} kT}} \qquad 3.60$$

where $F^{\ddagger}$ is the product of partition functions for all degrees of freedom of the activated complex except the degree of freedom along the reaction coordinate. Thus we have

$$\sum_j F_j^* k_j^{\ddagger} = \sum_n \tfrac{1}{2} F^{\ddagger} e^{-\frac{E_0^{\ddagger}}{kT}} \, e^{-\frac{n^2 h^2}{8\delta^2 m^{\ddagger} kT}} \, \frac{nh}{2\delta^2 m^{\ddagger}} \, \kappa_n + \sum_i e^{-\frac{\epsilon_i}{kT}} \, \nu_i \kappa_i \qquad 3.61$$

The last summation in Eq. 3.61 takes care of barrier leakage. The summation i is taken over all energy levels of the activated complex for which the energy along the reaction coordinate is below $n = 1$, the top of the barrier plus a zero point energy. If the factor κ_n is to be taken in front of the summation it must be given the appropriate mean value, $\bar{\kappa}_n$. Finally the summation over n in Eq. 3.61 can be replaced by an integral. Thus we obtain:

$$\sum_j F_j^* k_j^{\ddagger} = e^{-\frac{E_0^{\ddagger}}{kT}} \, F^{\ddagger} \bar{\kappa}_n \int_0^{\infty} e^{-\frac{n^2 h^2}{8\delta^2 m^{\ddagger} kT}} \, \frac{nh}{4\delta^2 m^{\ddagger}} \, dn + \sum_i e^{-\frac{\epsilon_i}{kT}} \, \nu_i \kappa_i$$

$$= \bar{\kappa}_n \, \frac{kT}{h} \, F^{\ddagger} e^{-\frac{\epsilon_a{}^{\ddagger}}{kT}} + \sum_i e^{-\frac{\epsilon_i}{kT}} \, \nu_i \kappa_i \qquad 3.62$$

$$\equiv \kappa \, \frac{kT}{h} \, F^{\ddagger} e^{-\frac{E_0^{\ddagger}}{kT}}$$

The last identity is, of course, a definition of κ and indicates that κ is ordinarily used to correct the theoretical rate of passage over the barrier for three effects: (a) reflection, (b) lack of equilibrium, both of which tend to decrease κ, and finally (c) barrier leakage, which tends to increase κ.

Rewriting Eq. 3.57 in the light of Eq. 3.62 we have for the rate of reaction, r, the familiar equation

$$r = \frac{c_1}{F_1} \frac{c_2}{F_2} \cdots \left(F^{\ddagger} e^{-\frac{E_0^{\ddagger}}{kT}} \bar{\kappa}_n \frac{kT}{h} + \sum_i e^{-\frac{\epsilon_i}{kT}} \nu_i \kappa_i \right)$$

$$= \frac{c_1}{F_1} \frac{c_2}{F_2} \cdots F^{\ddagger} \kappa \frac{kT}{h} e^{-\frac{E_0^{\ddagger}}{kT}} = c_1 c_2 \cdots K^{\ddagger} \kappa \frac{kT}{h}$$

$$\text{3.63}$$

$$= c_1 c_2 \cdots e^{-\frac{\Delta G^{\ddagger}}{RT}} \kappa \frac{kT}{h} = c_1 c_2 \cdots e^{-\frac{\Delta H^{\ddagger}}{RT}} e^{-\frac{\Delta S^{\ddagger}}{R}} \kappa \frac{kT}{h}$$

$$= c_1 c_2 \cdots e^{-\frac{\Delta G_1 + \int_1^p \Delta V^{\ddagger} dp}{RT}} \kappa \frac{kT}{h} = c_1 c_2 \cdots e^{-\frac{\Delta G_1^{\ddagger} + \overline{\Delta V^{\ddagger}}(p_1 - 1)}{RT}} \kappa \frac{kT}{h}$$

The third equality in Eq. 3.63 makes use of the fact that the equilibrium constant, $K^{\ddagger}$, between reactants and activated complexes has the value

$$K^{\ddagger} = \frac{F^{\ddagger}}{F_1 F_2 \cdots} e^{-\frac{E_0^{\ddagger}}{KT}} \qquad \text{3.64}$$

$F^{\ddagger}$ in Eq. 3.64, by definition, does not include the partition function for the reaction coordinate.

The fourth equality in Eq. 3.63 follows because of the thermodynamic relationship between the equilibrium constant, $K^{\ddagger}$, and the Gibbs free energy, $\Delta G^{\ddagger}$, which is $K^{\ddagger} = e^{-\frac{\Delta G^{\ddagger}}{RT}}$ The other equalities all make use of standard thermodynamic relations. Thus

$$\Delta G^{\ddagger} = \Delta H^{\ddagger} - T\Delta S^{\ddagger} = \Delta G_1^{\ddagger} + (p - 1)\Delta V^{\ddagger} \qquad \text{3.65}$$

Here $\Delta H^{\ddagger}$, $\Delta S^{\ddagger}$, $\Delta G_1^{\ddagger}$, $\Delta V^{\ddagger}$ and p are the heat of activation, entropy of activation, Gibbs free energy at one atmosphere, and pressure of the system, respectively.

It is convenient at this point to correct a common misconception. Arrhenius conceived of the activated state as being in equilibrium with reactants. Our present understanding of potential surfaces enables us to see that this simple view is incorrect. A metastable state such as the activated complex arising from reactants almost always goes on to products and does not equilibrate in the way characteristic of stable states. Instead, at equilibrium, products pass in the reverse direction through the metastable, activated states to maintain the balance characteristic of equilibrium. For example the rate for the step $H_2 + I_2 \rightarrow 2HI$ is essentially the same whether or not the reverse process $2HI \rightarrow H_2 + I_2$ occurs or is suppressed for the lack of HI. Further, the presence or absence of a slight depression at the top of the barrier is irrelevant for this argument. Should such a basin exist the metastable barriers on either side correspond to activated complex configurations, and we are still reduced to a consideration of metastable states as before. Thus there is no basis for treating the passage over a barrier by the simple equilibrium considerations of Arrhenius.

Barrier Leakage

Although chemical reaction by barrier leakage is negligibly small for many processes, there are other cases for which this is not true. The inversion of ammonia is such an example. The three NH bonds of ammonia make tetrahedral angles with each other. A fourth position which is filled by a proton in NH_4^+ remains vacant in the NH_3 molecule. Because of this vacant space, it is possible for the molecule to turn wrongside out like an umbrella in a windstorm. The barrier to be surmounted in such a switch is only about 7 kilocalories high, and it is sufficiently thin that leakage through the barrier is faster than passage over the top. The frequency of turning inside out is 2.387×10^{10} for the molecule in the quantum state specified by $J = 3$ and $K = 3$. This means that $\nu_i \kappa_i$ in Eq. 3.63 is just twice this observed frequency. Microwave absorption is a precise method for observing such frequencies. These frequencies also manifest themselves as splittings of spectral lines. Where optical methods are available for determining rates of inversion by measuring the splitting of spectral lines or by micro-wave measurements, greater accuracy can be achieved than by the usual methods of measuring chemical reactions.

Readings and References

Davidson, N., "Statistical Mechanics," McGraw-Hill Book Co., New York, 1962.

Eyring, H., Henderson, D. J., Stover, B. J., and Eyring, E. M., "Statistical Mechanics and Dynamics," John Wiley & Sons, Inc., New York, 1963.

Hill, T. L., "An Introduction to Statistical Thermodynamics," Addison-Wesley Publishing Co., Reading, Mass., 1960.

Rushbrooke, G. S., "Introduction to Statistical Mechanics," Oxford University Press, London, 1949.

Tolman, R. C., "The Principles of Statistical Mechanics," Oxford University Press, London, 1938.

chapter four

TRANSPORT MECHANISMS

Random Walk in Kinetics

A molecule that reacts to form two or more fragments by a unimolecular process ordinarily is excited to one of the energy-rich states which makes decomposition possible. This excitation is a result of a succession of random activating and deactivating collisions with neighboring molecules. Similarly, diffusion occurs because of random forward and backward displacements of the diffusing molecule, i.e., by a random walk process. It will be convenient to discuss diffusion and then generalize the results to other random walk processes.

Consider a molecule diffusing over a sequence of barriers as in Fig. 4.1. A diffusing molecule reaches a new equilibrium position at each new minimum after successfully passing from one ring of nearest neighbors to the next ring. Here we are using λ as a lattice distance. It should not be confused with the activity as used in the preceding chapter.

Consider the steady state regime in which there is a constant flux Q per square centimeter. This constant flux calculated at successive transition states, i.e., barrier maxima, leads to the following set of equations:

$$Q = \lambda_0 c_0 k_0 - \lambda_1 c_1 k_1' \qquad \text{(a)}$$

$$Q = \lambda_1 c_1 k_1 - \lambda_2 c_2 k_2' \qquad \text{(b)}$$

$$Q = \lambda_2 c_2 k_2 - \lambda_3 c_3 k_3' \qquad \text{(c)}$$

$$\vdots$$

$$Q = \lambda_{n-1} c_{n-1} k_{n-1} - \lambda_n c_n k_n' \qquad \text{(d)}$$

$$\left. \right\} \quad 4.1$$

Here $\lambda_i c_i$ is the number of molecules in the ith minimum per square centimeter of cross section while k_i and k_i' are the rate per second for a molecule at the ith minimum to jump forward and backward, respectively.

If Eq. (b) is multiplied by k_1'/k_1, Eq. (c) by $k_1' k_2'/(k_1 k_2)$ etc., and Eq. (d) by $\prod_{i=1}^{n-1} (k_i'/k_i)$ and all the equations are added together, the result is

$$Q = \frac{\lambda_0 c_0 k_0 - \lambda_n c_n k_n' \prod_{i=1}^{n-1} (k_i'/k_i)}{1 + \dfrac{k_1'}{k_1} + \dfrac{k_1' k_2'}{k_1 k_2} + \cdots \prod_{i=1}^{n-1} (k_i'/k_i)} \qquad 4.2$$

This kinetic approach to steady state problems as represented by Eq. 4.2 is an extremely powerful one and is generally applicable to steady-state processes. It leads to the same results as irreversible thermodynamics for systems near equilibrium, but has the great advantage that it also applies to systems far away from equilibrium. For the latter systems explicit account must be taken of the transition states which irreversible thermodynamics ignores. To understand the problem better, let us factor the specific rate constant into

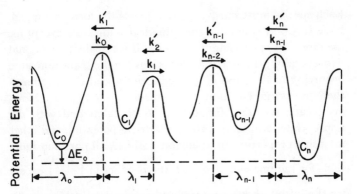

Fig. 4.1. A schematic sequence of potential barriers in the direction of flux for a molecule diffusing in the solid or liquid state.

the part characterizing the transition state and the part referring to the normal state. Thus

$$k_i = \left\{ \frac{\kappa k T_{i+1/2}}{h} F^{\ddagger}_{i+1/2} \exp\left(-E_{i+1/2}/k T_{i+1/2}\right) \right\} \left\{ F_i \exp\left(-E_i/k T_i\right) \right\}^{-1}$$

$$4.3$$

To calculate the first bracket which involves properties of the activated complex, one must use the properties such as temperature and electrical potential for the transition state, whereas in the second bracket the properties are for the initial state. If the Soret effect, which considers the concentration gradient developed due to a temperature gradient, is to be calculated by the use of Eq. 4.2 the flux, Q, for each species is set equal to zero. This requires that the corresponding numerator of Eq. 4.2 be set equal to zero. In this way, one obtains:

$$\frac{c_0}{c_n} = \frac{\lambda_n}{\lambda_0} \frac{k'_n}{k_0} \prod_{i=0}^{n-1} \left(\frac{k'_i}{k_i} \right) \qquad 4.4$$

Each species must satisfy an equation of the form of Eq. 4.4. Now k'_{i+1} and k_i involve the same transition state except for the direction of crossing the barrier. If we neglect directional irreversibility, the partition functions for the transition state occurring in the ratio k'_{i+1}/k_i cancel out and there remains the equilibrium constant between state $(i + 1)$ and i. However, each partition function is to be calculated with the appropriate local temperature, electrical potential, and other intensive properties. In analogous fashion, all partition functions for minima cancel out, in the product $\prod_{i=0}^{n-1} \left(\dfrac{k'_{i+1}}{k_i} \right)$ except for the initial and final state, and we are left with the ordinary equilibrium constant

$$\prod_{i=0}^{n-1} \left(\frac{k'_{i+1}}{k_i} \right) = e^{-\frac{G_n - G_0}{RT}} \qquad 4.5$$

The appropriate local temperatures, potentials and other intensive properties should be used in the calculation of the initial and final partition function or in the computation of the initial and final Gibbs free energies G_0 and G_n.

These considerations lead to the important conclusion that in the steady state the activity, i.e., the concentration of a molecule divided by its partition function per c.c., of each species, calculated for the local conditions is a constant throughout the system for all species which are not themselves flowing, even though other species (as well as heat and electricity) may be flowing. Matter in flux is also governed by Eq. 4.2 with enough gradient in the activities of species to give the attendant flux, Q. Under the near equilibrium conditions where irreversible thermodynamics is a useful approximation, irreversible thermodynamics and this kinetic approach yield the same results. However, when there are large gradients for temperatures, for electrical potential (or for chemical potential) or when the shear stress becomes large, only the kinetic approach is applicable. There are two reasons for this:

(1) With steep temperature gradients, it is by no means certain that the partition function for a transition state has the same value, i.e., has the same temperature, for crossing the barrier in one direction as it has for crossing in the reverse direction. This is because the transition state may reflect the temperature of the minimum from which it has just emerged. As explained above, this assumption of the canceling out of all partition function changes in the transition states while necessary in irreversible thermodynamics is not necessary in the kinetic approach. We next consider the second reason for greater generality of the kinetic approach.

(2) The current, Q, is only strictly proportional to the drop in free energy for low gradients of the free energy. Why this is true may be seen by considering Eq. 4.1b. When $Q = 0$, we have

$$0 = (\lambda_1 c_1 k_1)_0 - (\lambda_2 c_2 k_2')_0 \qquad 4.6$$

The subscript $_0$ is used to indicate $\Delta G = 0$ corresponding to zero flow. Now if the free energy of state 1 is increased over that of state 2 by ΔG a fraction β of ΔG will act to raise minimum 1 with respect to the transition state, while the final state will be correspondingly lowered with respect to the transition state by $(1 - \beta)\Delta G$, i.e., by the rest of the free energy. Neglecting any effect of ΔG on $(\lambda_1 c_1 k_1)_0$, we find that Eq. 4.1b takes the form:

$$Q = (\lambda_1 c_1 k_1)_0 \left(e^{-\beta \frac{\Delta G}{RT}} - e^{(1-\beta) \frac{\Delta G}{RT}} \right) \qquad 4.7$$

If ΔG is small, we can expand the exponentials and Eq. 4.7 becomes

$$Q = -(\lambda_1 c_1 k_1)_0 \frac{\Delta G}{RT} \qquad 4.8$$

This proportionality of flux to gradient of free energy holds so long as $\Delta G \ll RT$. ΔG may be made up of a chemical potential gradient $RT \ln a_0$ where the a's represent activities; it may be caused by a voltage drop and have the value $ZV23,069$ where Z and V are the valence and the voltage drop respectively; or ΔG may be a sum of these and other potential gradients.

Potential Gradients at Interfaces

An inspection of Eq. 4.2 and Fig. 4.1 will reveal that they can be applied to extremely complex situations. Consider an ion of valence Z_i crossing n uniformly high barriers across which an electrical potential V has been applied, giving rise to a current, I_i. The convention with respect to the sign of the potential, V, is defined here by the equation $\Delta G = Z_i V23,069$ where Z_i is the valence of the ion which is flowing. Which sign is adopted for the potential, V, is of no consequence so long as there is consistency throughout. Equation 4.2 then takes the form:

$$I_i = Z_i 96,500(\lambda_0 k_0)_i$$

$$\frac{e^{-\frac{Z_i V23,069}{2nRT}}\left(c_0 - c_n e^{\frac{Z_i V23,069}{RT}}\right)}{1 + e^{\frac{Z_i V23,069}{nRT}} + e^{\frac{2Z_i V23,069}{nRT}} + \cdots + e^{\frac{n-1}{n}\frac{Z_i V23,069}{RT}}} \qquad 4.9$$

The concentrations c_0 and c_n should be in moles per c.c. in order that I_i should be amperes per square centimeters.

The denominator of Eq. 4.9 has the value $\dfrac{1 - e^{\frac{Z_i V23,069}{RT}}}{1 - e^{\frac{Z_i V23,069}{nRT}}}$

Multiplying numerator and denominator of Eq. 4.9 by $e^{-\frac{Z_i V23,069}{2RT}}$ gives

$$I_i = Z_i 96{,}500(\lambda_0 k_0 g)_i \left(c_0 e^{-\frac{Z_i V 23{,}069}{2RT}} - c_n e^{\frac{Z_i V 23{,}069}{2RT}} \right) \qquad 4.10$$

where

$$g_i = \frac{e^{-\frac{Z_i V 23{,}069}{2RT}} - e^{\frac{Z_i V 23{,}069}{2RT}}}{e^{-\frac{Z_i V 23{,}069}{2nRT}} - e^{\frac{Z_i V 23{,}069}{2nRT}}} \approx n \quad \text{as} \quad V \to 0 \qquad 4.11$$

Eq. 4.10 can be rewritten as

$$I_i = p_i \left(c_0 e^{-\frac{Z_i V 23{,}069}{2RT}} - c_n e^{\frac{Z_i V 23{,}069}{2RT}} \right) \qquad 4.12$$

Here our effective permeability $|p_i| = |Z_i|96{,}500(\lambda_0 k_0 g)_i$ is conveniently measured in the units ampere centimeters but p_i itself carries a plus or minus sign paralleling the sign of the valence, Z_i. The total current density, I, at any interface is the sum of the current densities for all ions

$$I = \sum_i I_i \qquad 4.13$$

If we solve Eq. 4.13 for the interesting case $I = 0$ using Eq. 4.12 to define I_i we obtain:

$$V = \frac{RT}{Z 23{,}069} \ln \frac{\sum_j |p_j| c_j e^{-(|Z_j| - Z)\frac{V 23{,}069}{2RT}}}{\sum_i |p_i| c_i e^{(|Z_i| - Z)\frac{V 23{,}069}{2RT}}} \qquad 4.14$$

This equation was developed by Funk, Giddings, Christensen, and Eyring (1957) in their studies of strain electrometry.

The summation over j is over all currents which tend to increase the positive charge on position 0 and summation i is over all terms which tend to increase the negative charge on position 0. The term Z is chosen so as to make as many of the exponents in Eq. 4.14 vanish as is possible. If all the $|Z_i|$'s are equal to each other and then, of course, to Z, then every exponent in Eq. 4.14 vanishes, and it is trivially easy to solve Eq. 4.14. The simplified form of Eq. 4.14 where all Z's are equal was derived by Goldman (1943) in a quite different way. When all $|Z_i|$'s are not equal, it is still possible to solve Eq. 4.14 by successive approximations. When a single reaction and its reverse are much faster than all others, Eq. 4.14 reduces to the usual Nernst equation

$$V = \frac{RT}{Z23,069} \ln \frac{c_0}{c_n} \qquad 4.15$$

Here if c_0 is the effective concentration of the standard electrode having the potential $V_0 = \dfrac{RT}{Z23,069} \ln c_0$ then equation (15) takes the familiar form

$$V = -\frac{RT}{Z23,069} \ln c_n + V_0 \qquad 4.16$$

Strictly we should use the effective concentrations, i.e., the activities rather than the concentrations in calculating V and V_0.

We now have developed the necessary background to discuss corrosion, strain electrometry, the glass electrode, smelting, nerve conduction, photography, and other types of interfacial potential.

Corrosion and Strain Electrometry

In corrosion we have a situation quite different from that of the simple Nernst potential in which the forward reaction is balanced by its own back reaction. Thus, in place of the equilibrium potential, we have a more or less steady potential in which the negative charge left on the metal by dissolving positive ions is removed not only by the returning positive metal ions but also by the action of a substance such as oxygen as it takes up the electrons from the metal and reacts with water to make hydroxyl ions which in turn react with the metal ions to precipitate hydroxide. If the precipitated hydroxide forms a protecting oxide layer, as in the case of aluminum, the corrosion may come to a virtual standstill. If this oxide layer is broken under water by scratching, or by some other type of strain, the bare aluminum develops a potential slightly in excess of a volt more negative than before, in less than a hundredth of a second. In the course of about a second this potential will decay, roughly exponentially, back to the resting value as a new oxide layer heals over the broken surface area.

This voltage change can be understood by a glance at Eq. 4.14. The potential, V, is suddenly changed by the strain not because of the slight change by a millivolt or so in the activity of the metal atoms but because the ratio of permeability $|p_j|$ for aluminum ions to the permeability $|p_i|$ for electrons is suddenly increased by a factor of 10^{17}. Clearly the oxide film prevents corrosion because it is such an effective barrier to migration of the aluminum ions. Because of the semiconducting character of the oxide layer it presents no comparable barrier to the flow of negative charge. Rupture of the oxide layer lowers the free energy of activation for diffusion of Al ions through the barrier by a volt more than it lowers the free energy of activation against electron diffusion. This increase in the relative permeability to positive as compared with negative currents through the barrier varies continuously with the degree of rupture of the oxide film. Factors that influence the voltage developed are the amount of strain, the pH, the concentration of oxygen, and the other constituents dissolved in the water. It is also possible to protect the surface of metals by making $|p_j|$, the permeability for aluminum ions, small by using all kinds of protective coatings of ions and organic materials. The economic losses from the corrosion of metals in this country alone, are estimated to be in excess of five billion dollars a year. It is, therefore, a matter of major importance to understand and prevent such losses.

Smelting

In the smelting process a pool of molten iron at around $1500°$ C is overlain by a molten slag composed chiefly of Al_2O_3, SiO_2 and CaO. If this material is enclosed in a carbon vessel from which the CO formed can escape, a variety of chemical reactions are found to take place. Typically the iron will contain small amounts of dissolved sulfur and carbon. The smelting process then proceeds in the following way. Oxygen ions diffuse from the slag and combine with carbon to form CO which then escapes as a gas leaving the oxygen electronic charge on the metal. The resulting electrical potential tends to slow down the evolution of CO except when the negative charge on the metal is used up by sulfur (dissolved in the iron that is changing to sulfide ions which coincidentally migrate into the slag) or by metal ions (such as Si^{++} and Fe^{++}) that are migrating from the slag into the molten metal where they become electrically neutral.

To work out this electrochemical theory of smelting we must adapt Eq. 4.10 to the diffusion across the slag-metal interface of the various constituents. In this way we get the following equations:

$$-n_{Fe,m} = n_{Fe,s} = k_{Fe}a_{Fe,m} \exp\left\{\tfrac{2}{2}VF/RT\right\} - k_{Fe}a_{Fe,s} \exp\left\{-\tfrac{2}{2}VF/RT\right\}$$
$$4.17$$

$$-n_{Si,m} = n_{Si,s} = k_{Si}a_{Si,m} \exp\left\{\tfrac{4}{2}VF/RT\right\} - k_{Si}a_{Si,s} \exp\left\{-\tfrac{4}{2}VF/RT\right\}$$
$$4.18$$

$$-n_{O,s} = n_{CO} = k_O a_{O,s} \exp\left\{\tfrac{2}{2}VF/RT\right\}$$
$$4.19$$

$$-n_{S,m} = n_{S,s} = k_S a_{S,m} \exp\left\{-\tfrac{2}{2}VF/RT\right\} - k_S a_{S,s} \exp\left\{\tfrac{2}{2}VF/RT\right\}$$
$$4.20$$

In these equations V is the difference between the voltages of the melt and slag. The suffix m signifies quantities related to the melt while suffix s is for the slag. Thus $a_{Si,m}$, for example, indicates the activity of silicon ion in the melt. Also $n_{Fe,s}$ indicates the rate of increase of iron in the slag.

In a very complete set of experiments, King and Ramachandran (1958) measured simultaneously the amount of iron, silicon, and sulfur transferred between melt and slag and the amount of CO gas evolved.

Using Eqs. 4.17 through 4.20 in integrated form, de Hemptinne, Eyring, and Ree were able to calculate the rate of migration of iron, silicon, and sulfur between phases from the observed rate of evolution of carbon monoxide. The measurement of the rate of evolution of CO provides also a value for the potential across the interface in accord with Eq. 4.19. Conversely, a measurement of the voltage would enable one to calculate the rate of migration of all substances including CO. In Fig. 4.2 we compare the experimental results of one of the runs of King and Ramachandran (1958) with the calculated values for iron and silicon by de Hemptinne, Eyring and Ree (1961).

Photographic Development

Development of the latent photographic image is a process closely paralleling the smelting process. The developable image is a small cluster of silver atoms, sometimes including gold, formed by photochemical reduction of an appropriate salt, frequently a halide. For a latent image to be developable, it must contain enough metal atoms to permit it to accept extra electrons in the same way that bulk metals do. If the metal aggregates are too small to be developed, the addition of a salt of monovalent gold will result in the reduction of some gold which precipitates out on the image.

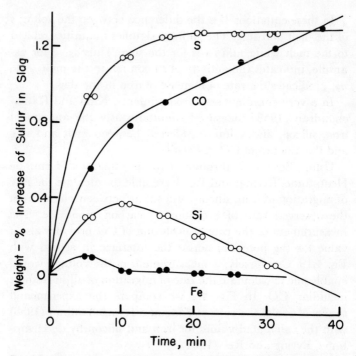

Fig. 4.2. A comparison of the theory (curves) of de Hemptinne, Eyring and Ree for the smelting process with the experimental data (points) of King and Rama-chandran (1958) at 1505° C. The weight per cent increase of sulfur in the slag is plotted versus time. The ordinate scales for the evolution of carbon monoxide and for the transfer of iron and silicon to the slag are converted into an equivalent weight per cent increase for sulfur. Slag composition: 48% CaO, 21% Al_2O_3 and 31% SiO_2. (Reproduced by permission from de Hemptinne, Eyring, and Ree in "Physical Chemistry of Process Metallurgy," vol. 7, part 1, G. R. St. Pierre, ed., Interscience Publishers, Inc., New York, 1960.)

The developer frequently contains substances like sodium sulfide which slowly dissolves the halide crystals bringing silver ions into solution. The silver ions migrate to the latent image in the same way that iron ions dissolved in a slag migrate to the molten metals and are there reduced to metal atoms. In some cases silver salts, such as silver nitrate, are added to the developer. In any case the silver ions are reduced on the latent image, and analogous to Eq. 4.17 of the smelting process is the equation

$$n_{Ag,m} = k_{Ag}a_{Ag,s} \exp\left\{-\tfrac{1}{2}VF/RT\right\} - k_{Ag}a_{Ag,m} \exp\left\{\tfrac{1}{2}VF/RT\right\} \qquad 4.21$$

The developing solution contains large concentrations of some reducing agent RH_2, frequently hydroquinone, which releases protons to the solution leaving the liberated electrons on the latent image where they reduce metal ions. The parallel in the smelting process is the oxidation of oxygen ions from the slag by carbon with liberation of electrons to the melt. This liberation of electrons from RH_2 can be expressed by an equation:

$$n_e = k_{RH_2}a_{RH_2} \exp\left\{\tfrac{2}{3}VF/RT\right\} - k_R a_R (a_{H^+})^2 \exp\left\{-\tfrac{2}{3}VF/RT\right\} \qquad 4.22$$

The electrochemical model thus also embraces photography.

The Glass Electrode

Inspection of Eq. 4.14 shows that when the permeability of a membrane to one ion greatly exceeds that of other ions two electrodes placed in the electrolytic solutions of reservoirs on the two sides of the membranes measure a voltage

$$V = \frac{RT}{Z23,069} \ln \frac{a_j}{a_i} \qquad 4.23$$

Here a_j and a_i are the activities, i.e., the effective concentrations in the two reservoirs of the permeable ion. When other ions have comparable values for the products, activities times permeabilities, the observed potential must be calculated from Eq. 4.14 rather than from Eq. 4.23. By suitably selecting thin glass membranes of the proper composition, we can make them almost exclusively permeable to hydrogen so that the measured voltage relates the unknown pH in one reservoir to that in the standard reservoir on the other side of the glass membrane. Careful equalizing of the concentration of the most permeable ion on the two sides of a membrane can change the situation so that the voltage now reflects the relative concentrations in the two reservoirs of a less permeable ion in accord with Eq. 4.14. Various other interesting uses of membranes permeable to ions will be suggested by Eq. 4.14.

Potentials Across Biological Membranes

Living cells are surrounded by membranes 50 to 100 Å thick. The membrane consists of a layer of lipids, such as lecithin, sandwiched in between two protein layers. The cells vary in size from nerve cells with lengths approximating the length of an arm or leg to others which are very small. Typically, cells are a few microns in diameter. Since all cells are nourished by diffusion this places severe restrictions on the possible maxima for at least one dimension of the cell. Because a difference in composition is maintained between the inside and outside of the semipermeable membrane surrounding a living cell, as a result of metabolic processes, it is inevitable, in view of Eq. 4.14, that potential differences should develop with the induced gradients in ionic concentrations across the membrane.

A typical cell is about 80 millivolts more negative inside than out. Potassium is about 30 times more concentrated inside the cell than out, in rough accord with Nernst's equation. Sodium, on the other hand, is apt to be 30 times more concentrated outside than in, in definite disagreement with Nernst's equation. Ions which fail to obey the Nernst equation are said to be pumped or to show active transport.

Returning to Eq. 4.14, we can again find the explanation. Sodium ions are ordinarily solvated with water and in this state find the resting membrane quite impermeable. Inside the cell where substances are synthesized by metabolic processes, one of these products, the pump substance, presumably coordinates with the sodium ion, thus replacing water and endowing the complexed sodium ion with high permeability. Outside the cell the pump substance is chemically modified so that it prefers to complex with potassium for the return journey. Thus we have two kinds of sodium ions, the nonpermeable, water-coordinated variety and the permeable variety coordinated with pump substance. The relative concentrations inside and outside the cell of the permeable sodium ion closely approximates the ratio expected from the Nernst equation for the observed voltage. Thus sodium ions are pumped by metabolites establishing a gradient of soluble ions coordinated with pump substance such that the gradient causes sodium to diffuse outside the cell. Other more permeable ions then adjust their concentration gradients to the potential induced by the pumped ions. Equation 4.14 thus provides a good basis for understanding the potentials across nerve membranes as well as across the membranes of other cells. Hodgkin and Huxley (1952) were able to account quantitatively for the resting potentials of nerve cells and for nerve conduction by using in addition to the ideas discussed above the fact that permeability for the various ions is determined by and varies strongly with the voltage.

Potentials of up to 500 volts developed by organisms such as the electric eel arise from some 5000 cell potentials arranged in series. 5000 cells piled on top of each other develop no potential because the potential across the membrane on top of the cells just neutralizes the potential across the bottom, but if the top membrane of each cell in such a pile is suddenly made permeable and thus shorted out, the potentials of the bottom membranes now act in series to give the observed potential. The nervous system of the eel is hooked up to each top membrane of a pile of cells in such a way as to short them out by a nerve impulse and thereby deliver the resulting high voltages through its electric organ.

Many more cases could be discussed, but this should suffice to show the power of the kinetic approach when applied to problems involving diffusion, electrical potentials, and other types of potential gradients.

Readings and References

De Hemptinne, X., Eyring, H., and Ree, T., "The Electrochemical Theory of Smelting and Related Reactions," in "Physical Chemistry of Process Metallurgy," vol. 8, part 1, G. R. St. Pierre, ed., Interscience Publishers, Inc., New York, 1960.

Eyring, H., "The Physical Chemistry of Nerve Action," in "Molecular Biology," D. Nachmansohn, ed., Academic Press, New York, 1960.

Funk, A. G., Giddings, J. C., Christensen, C. J., and Eyring, H., "Strain Electrometry and Corrosion I. General Considerations on Interfacial Electrical Transients," *Proc. Natl. Acad. Sci.,* **43,** 421 (1957).

Goldman, D. E., "Potential, Impedance, and Rectification in Membranes," *J. Gen. Physiol.,* **27,** 37 (1943).

Hodgkin, A. L., and Huxley, A. F., "A Quantitative Description of Membrane Current and Its Application to Conduction and Excitation in Nerve," *J. Physiol.,* **117,** 500 (1952).

King, T. B., and Ramachandran, S., "Electrochemical Nature of Sulfur Transfer in the System Carbon-Saturated-Iron–Slag," in "The Physical Chemistry of Steelmaking," J. F. Elliott, ed., Technology Press, Cambridge, Mass. and John Wiley & Sons, New York, 1958.

Parlin, R. B., and Eyring, H., "Membrane Permeability and Electrical Potential," in "Ion Transport Across Membranes," H. T. Clarke, ed., Academic Press, New York, 1954.

chapter five

SOME THERMODYNAMIC ASPECTS
OF CHEMICAL REACTIONS

Biological Reactions

Most enzyme-catalyzed reactions show a temperature optimum. The Arrhenius equation predicts that an elementary reaction will speed up exponentially with temperature over the entire temperature range. Clearly, biological reactions showing the customary temperature optimum must be complex. Typical of oxidative enzymic reactions is bioluminescence. Familiar examples of bioluminescence are the firefly, the glowworm, and various types of luminescent organisms in the sea. Exemplifying the latter is the small crustacean *Cypridina* found off the coast of Japan. About forty of these small creatures cover an average thumb nail. A cold extract of crushed *Cypridina* luminesces for a while and then fades out. A hot extract gives no light, but if cooled and added to the spent cold extract, light is again emitted.

The cold extract when purified yields the enzyme, luciferase, with a molecular weight of about 70,000 as shown by Chase and Langridge (1960). Since the constituent amino acids have average molecular weights of about 100, the enzyme is a linear polymer of about 700 units coiled like a rope into helices with slightly under 4 monomers to a turn. If six such helices formed piles packed around a central pile, with 24 loops in each pile, one would have something like the compact structure of an enzyme in its native state. The enzyme is folded so that its polar groups extend out into the water, and the hydrophobic groups are buried inside the coils, making contact with adjacent hydrophobic groups.

If the temperature is raised the enzyme molecule unfolds, losing its catalytic activity and is said to be denatured. From a hot extract, by purification, luciferin can be abstracted. Luciferin prepared from different species differs, but, for example, *Cypridina luciferin* has the empirical formula $C_{21}H_{28}O_2N_6 \cdot 2HCl$ and the provisional structure (Johnson, *et al.*, 1961)

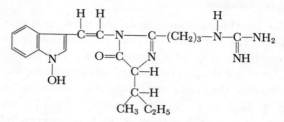

Many varieties of single cells luminesce. Examples are *Photobacterium phosphoreum*, *Vibrio phosphorescens* and *A. fischeri* among others. In Fig. 5.1 the effect of pressure and temperature on the luminescence of *Photobacterium phosphorescence* is compared with theory with gratifying results.

It will be instructive to develop the theory of luminescence. Since luminescence is an enzyme-catalyzed oxidation of luciferin, LH_2, by active luciferase, A_n, it would be natural to expect the light intensity, I, to be proportional to the concentration of reactants. This is true except for oxygen. Bacterial luminescence is independent of oxygen pressure at pressures of oxygen above about 10^{-10} atmospheres. This

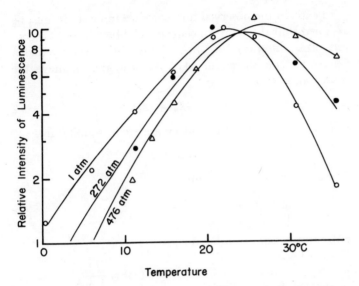

Fig. 5.1. The brightness of luminescence in *Photobacterium phosphoreum* as a function of temperature at three different hydrostatic pressures. The points represent data from experiments by Brown, Johnson, and Marsland (1942). The smooth curves were calculated by Eyring and Magee (1942) in accordance with Eq. 5.8. (Reproduced by permission from Johnson, F. H., Eyring, H., and Polissar, M. J., "The Kinetic Basis of Molecular Biology," p. 25, John Wiley & Sons, Inc., New York, 1954.)

means that at the higher pressures, where luminescence is independent of oxygen, luciferase can acquire oxygen molecules faster than it acquires the luciferin which is to be oxidized. We are accordingly led to the equation:

$$I = bk'(A_n)(\mathrm{LH_2}) \qquad 5.1$$

Here k' is the specific rate constant for the reactions, and b is a proportionality factor determined by the units used and by the fact that about every tenth luciferin molecule which is oxidized emits radiation.

To explain the observed luminescence intensity it must be assumed that the total concentration of luciferase (A_o) consists of a concentration, (A_n), of the native variety and a denatured concentration, (A_d). Accordingly, we have the conservation equation

$$(A_o) = (A_n) + (A_d) \qquad 5.2$$

Since native and denatured luciferase are in equilibrium,

$$A_n \rightleftharpoons A_d$$

The equation for equilibrium is

$$\frac{(A_d)}{(A_n)} = K \qquad 5.3$$

Substituting Eq. 5.3 in Eq. 5.2 gives

$$(A_o) = (A_n) + K(A_n) \quad \text{or} \quad (A_n) = \frac{(A_o)}{1 + K} \qquad 5.4$$

Finally introducing Eq. 5.4 into Eq. 5.1 gives

$$I = \frac{bk'(A_o)(\text{LH}_2)}{1 + K} \qquad 5.5$$

In accord with Eq. 3.63 the expression for k' is

$$k' = \kappa \frac{kT}{h} e^{-\frac{\Delta H_0^{\ddagger}}{RT}} e^{\frac{\Delta S_0^{\ddagger}}{R}} e^{-\frac{\overline{\Delta V}^{\ddagger}(p-1)}{RT}} \qquad 5.6$$

and

$$K = e^{-\frac{\Delta H_0}{RT}} e^{\frac{\Delta S_0}{R}} e^{-\frac{(p-1)\overline{\Delta V}}{RT}} \qquad 5.7$$

Substituting Eqs. 5.6 and 5.7 into 5.5 gives

$$I = \frac{aTe^{-\frac{\Delta H_0^{\ddagger}}{RT}} e^{-\frac{\overline{\Delta V}^{\ddagger}(p-1)}{RT}}}{1 + e^{-\frac{\Delta H_0}{RT}} e^{\frac{\Delta S_0}{R}} e^{-\frac{(p-1)\overline{\Delta V}}{RT}}} \qquad 5.8$$

Here $a = \left\{ (LH_2)(A_o) \kappa \dfrac{k}{h} e^{\frac{\Delta S_0^{\ddagger}}{R}} \right\}$ is a constant which must be chosen to fit the data.

To obtain the agreement shown in Fig. 5.1 the following values were found by Eyring and Magee (1942)

$\Delta H_0^{\ddagger} = 17.22$ kcal, $\overline{\Delta V^{\ddagger}} = 546.4 - 1.813T$ ml

$\Delta H_0 = 55.26$ kcal, $\overline{\Delta V} = -922.8 + 3.206T$ ml, $\Delta S_0 = 184$ eu

A reasonable picture of the reaction leading to luminescence is that below the optimum temperature the enzyme is folded in the active native state. There must be two active sites on the enzyme. The oxygen must adsorb on one site with the luciferin on a neighboring site. As the luciferin releases protons into the solution the electrons are taken up by the oxygen with the aid of the enzyme. About nine times out of ten the outermost electrons are captured by the oxygen. The tenth time an inner electron is removed and the remaining outer electron drops into the empty level beneath, thus emitting a photon. When the enzyme unfolds due to heating or because of the presence of a denaturing agent the conformation shifts making the enzyme ineffective as a catalyst.

When narcotics such as the alcohols, ethers, or ketones are added to luminescent bacteria, their light is dimmed. All of these agents have a hydrophobic hydrocarbon portion joined to a hydrogen bond-forming section. The dimming of the luminescence results from inactivation of the luciferase as it forms hydrophobic bonds with about three molecules of an alcohol or some other active agent. Such bonds shift the enzyme equilibrium from the native to the denatured state by lowering the surface tension at the interface between enzyme and solvent and so favoring the extended denatured state. This dimming of luminescence by a narcotic, N, results from the forming of an additional inactive enzyme species.

The new species containing s narcotic molecules must be taken account of in the conservation equation, thus:

$$(A_o) = (A_n) + (A_d) + (A_dN_s) \qquad 5.9$$

Further we have

$$A_d + sN \rightleftharpoons A_dN_s \qquad 5.10$$

for which the equilibrium constant is K_3 and

$$(A_dN_s) = K_3(A_d)(N)^s = K_3K(A_n)(N)^s \qquad 5.11$$

Hence

$$(A_o) = (A_n) + K(A_n) + K_3K(A_n)(N)^s \qquad 5.12$$

or

$$(A_n) = \frac{A_o}{1 + K + K_3K(N)^s} \qquad 5.13$$

The light intensity, I_N, in the presence of a narcotic is therefore

$$I_N = \frac{bk'(\mathrm{LH_2})(A_o)}{1 + K + K_3K(N)^s} \qquad 5.14$$

so that

$$\frac{I}{I_N} = \frac{1 + K + K_3K(N)^s}{1 + K} \qquad 5.15$$

or

$$\ln\left\{\left(\frac{I}{I_N} - 1\right)\left(\frac{1 + K}{K}\right)\right\} = \ln K_3 + s \ln (N)$$

$$= -\frac{\Delta H_3}{RT} + \frac{\Delta S_3}{R} + s \ln N \qquad 5.16$$

By plotting the experimental quantity on the left of Eq. 5.16 against $\frac{1}{T}$ and against $\ln N$, one determines ΔH_3 and s respectively; finally ΔS_3 is obtained from the remainder. For 0.4 M in alcohol solutions containing *Photobacterium phosphorium* Johnson, Eyring, Steblay, *et al.* (1945) found $s = 2.7$, $\Delta H_3 = -37$ kcal, $\Delta S_3 = -128$ e.u.

If *Photobacterium phosphorium* are inhibited by alcohol and then subjected to a few hundred atmospheres pressure, the light comes on just as it does when heat-denatured bacteria are subjected to hydrostatic pressure. Much of the effect of alcohol and ether on people is caused by partial inactivation of the oxidative enzymes concerned with the respiration of the brain and therefore with consciousness. For example, tadpoles and salamanders can be made drunk with alcohol and can then be sobered instantly by applying hydrostatic pressure. However, when the pressure is released, they instantly sink back into a drunken stupor (Johnson and Flagler, 1951).

It is important to realize that, while we have chosen luminescence to illustrate the effect of temperature, pressure, and various inhibitors on oxidative enzymes, these effects are general. Parallel effects are found on the chirping of a cricket, the crawling of an ant, or the evolution of CO_2 from rat brains. Many other biological examples are given by Johnson, Eyring, and Polissar (1954). However, we must go on to other examples of reaction kinetics.

Evaporation and Condensation

The number of gas molecules hitting a sq cm per sec, Z, is equal to one half the number of molecules per cc, $n/2V$, multiplied by the average velocity along the normal to the surface, $\bar{x}$. According to the Wilson-Sommerfeld quantization rule,

$$nh = 2m\dot{x}l \qquad \text{or} \qquad \dot{x} = nh/2ml \qquad 5.17$$

and

$$\bar{x} = \sum_{n=1}^{\infty} \frac{nh}{2ml} e^{-\frac{n^2h^2}{8l^2mkT}} \bigg/ \sum_{n=1}^{\infty} e^{-\frac{n^2h^2}{8l^2mkT}}$$

$$= \int_0^{\infty} \frac{nh}{2ml} e^{-\frac{n^2h^2}{8l^2mkT}} dn \bigg/ \int_0^{\infty} e^{-\frac{n^2h^2}{8l^2mkT}} dn = \sqrt{\frac{2kT}{\pi m}}$$

5.18

According to the perfect gas-law, one writes,

$$p/kT = n/V$$

5.19

Thus

$$Z = \frac{p}{2kT} \sqrt{\frac{2kT}{\pi m}} = \frac{p}{\sqrt{2\pi mkT}}$$

5.20

If s is the fraction of colliding molecules which stick, then the rate of sticking per sq cm per sec, r, is

$$r = sZ = \frac{sp}{\sqrt{2\pi mkT}}$$

5.21

An especially simple example of such considerations is the rate of condensation of a vapor on its own liquid surface. The act of condensation of a molecule is one in which one vapor molecule disappears and one bulk liquid molecule appears. Although the condensing molecule probably stays on the surface, this does not increase the total number of surface molecules, since the molecule just below the new surface molecule has ceased to be a surface molecule. Thus successful condensation of a molecule involves not only collision with the surface but a loss of translational energy from the reaction coordinate and adjustment of the rotational degrees of freedom from their condition in the vapor to the condition in the bulk liquid. The sticking coefficient, s, may consequently be thought of as a product of factors for the adjustment of the various degrees of freedom to their new condition. Both calculations and experiment indicate a very high probability, approximately unity, for deactivation of the reaction coordinate. Thus a molecule should stick whenever the proper conditions are fulfilled for the rotational degrees of freedom. If in the activated state a molecule must have the rotational partition function of the liquid in order to stick, the rate of sticking

$$r = sp/\sqrt{2\pi mkT}$$

must have in it the ratio

$$\delta = f_{rl}/f_{rv} \qquad\qquad 5.22$$

where f_{rl} is the molecular partition function of the liquid and f_{rv} that of the gas. George Wyllie (1949) observed that the free angle ratio $\delta = f_{rl}/f_{rv}$ of Kincaid and Eyring (1938) did in fact give the sticking coefficient for a wide variety of liquids ranging from CCl_4 (which rotates freely so that $\delta = 1$) to hydrogen-bonded liquids which have values of δ in the neighborhood of 0.04. Mortensen and Eyring (1960) have found Eq. 5.22 to be widely applicable. A portion of a table from their paper is given in Table 5.1.

Heideger and Boudart (1961) have recently carried out a careful experimental investigation of the evaporation of glycerol. They agree with earlier measurements and with the theory developed by Mortensen and Eyring.

The reverse of condensation is evaporation. While condensation is an association reaction, evaporation is a unimolecular decomposition. The successful calculation of a sticking coefficient for condensation means that the rate of evaporation is also determined, since the ratio of the two rates is equal to the equilibrium constant. There is thus no difficulty in the calculation of the transmission coefficients for such reactions.

When gaseous nitrogen strikes a tungsten wire, the prob-

TABLE 5.1. Comparison of Free Angle Ratios

Molecule	Tc, °K	T, °C	δ (Kincaid and Eyring)	s (obsd.)[a]
CCl_4	556.31	0	1.02	1(0)[b,c,d,e]
		50	1.31	
C_6H_6	561.7	0	0.86	0.85–0.95(6)[f]
		50	1.14	
$CHCl_3$	536	0	0.26	.16(2)[f]
		50	.99	
CH_3I	528	0	.37	
		40	1.25	
CH_3OH	513.4	0	0.034	.045(0)[f]
		50	.048	
C_2H_5OH	516.3	0	.019	0.24(13)[g]
		50	.028	.036(0)[e]
H_2O	647.31	0	.022	.036(15)[h]
		100	.17	.02(100)[d]
CH_3COCH_3	508.2	0	.16	
		50	.54	
Cyclo-C_6H_{12}	553.9	10	.69	
		80	1.55	
n-C_6H_{14}	507.9	0	0.57	
		50	.99	
n-C_7H_{16}	540.17	0	.23	
		50	.36	
$C_6H_5CH_3$	594.0	0	.60	
		50	.91	
n-C_3H_7OH	536.9	0	.008	.037[f]
		100	.030	

[a] A number in parentheses in the last column is the temperature (°C) at which the condensation coefficient was measured. [b] T. Alty and F. H. Nicoll, *Can. J. Research,* **4,** 547 (1931). [c] T. Alty, *Phil. Mag.,* **15,** 82 (1933). [d] W. Pruger, *Z. Physik,* **115,** 202 (1940). [e] L. von Bogdandy, H. C. Kleist and O. Knake, *Z. Elektrochem.,* **59,** 460 (1955). [f] M. Baranaev, *J. Phys. Chem.* (U.S.S.R.), **13,** 1035 (1939). [g] H. Bucka, *Z. Physik. Chem.,* **195,** 260 (1950). [h] T. Alty and C. A. Mackay, *Proc. Roy. Soc.* (London), **A149,** 104 (1935).

lem of a sticking coefficient again arises. Careful experimental results of Ehrlich (1961) and other investigators indicate that substantially every nitrogen molecule striking tungsten undergoes a weak physical adsorption and that subsequently there is competition between reevaporation and stronger molecular and atomic adsorptions. The weak physical adsorption of nitrogen is a gas like state in which the molecules, even though they are rotating, are still adsorbed at least temporarily. Such a state doesn't seem to exist for liquids. Wanlass (1962), working in this laboratory, has developed a theory for this type of adsorption. It is natural to compare condensation with other types of association reactions. In Table 5.2 taken from the work of T. S. Ree, *et al.* (1962), we see in most cases quite close agreement between experiment and calculations for rates of association reactions in which each of the associating radicals are assumed to be freely rotating in the activated state. In the last two cases where there is disagreement in $\Delta S_b^{\ddagger}$, the activation entropy of the backward reaction, there is apparently restricted rotation of the associating radicals in the activated complex.

It is not possible in this brief treatment to consider the many other well-understood types of chemical reactions. Instead we will close with a few general considerations.

The Mapping of Configurational Energy as a Landscape

It is impossible to obtain a solution in closed form for the motion of even three bodies in a potential field. This famous astronomical problem has remained unsolved through the centuries. Needless to say, the problem retains its complications when quantum mechanics is substituted for classical mechanics and becomes even more intractable with the more than three atoms entering into most chemical reactions. Nevertheless for those regions of configuration space where the potential energy can be expressed with sufficient accuracy, as a quadratic, analytical solutions are obtained. In this way both at minima, corresponding to stable molecules, and at saddle points one gets solutions in terms of the well-known normal modes of vibration. As explained earlier, the

TABLE 5.2. Radical Association Reactions at 400° K

	$k_f \times 10^{-13}$ (obs.) (cc/mole sec)	$k_f \times 10^{-13}$ (calc.) (cc/mole sec)	ΔS_b eu	$\Delta S_b^{\ddagger}$ (theoret.) eu	$\Delta S_b^{\ddagger}$ (exptl.) eu
(1) $CH_3 + CH_3 \rightarrow C_2H_6$	2.2	4.8κ	17.73	19.98	15.68
(2) $C_2H_5 + C_2H_5 \rightarrow C_4H_{10}$	2.0	4.7κ	24.50	26.73	22.27
(3) $CH_3 + C_2H_5 \rightarrow C_3H_8$	4.2	9.7κ	21.19	24.86	20.43
(4) $CF_3 + CF_3 \rightarrow C_2F_6$	2.3	2.3κ	24.28	25.04	22.33
(5) $NO_2 + NO_2 \rightarrow N_2O_4$	0.05	3.0κ	21.11	22.45	11.54
(6) $CH_3 + NO \rightarrow CH_3NO$	0.02	7.1κ	14.02	17.06	2.64

normal mode transverse to the energy barrier at the transition state is called the reaction coordinate. It, of course, has a negative value for the square of its frequency, while the square of all other frequencies are positive. The reaction coordinate can be thought of as a fourth translational degree of freedom belonging to the activated complex. The activated complex persists only for the fleeting instant during which the system passes through the transition state.

The great importance of the equilibrium concept of reaction kinetics is that it can be formulated in terms of the activated complex in equilibrium with the reactants and for all these species the mechanical equations of motion are soluble by the use of the theory of small vibrations. In this way a very nasty problem in mechanics is solved by invoking the equilibrium concept, and tucking any loose ends into the transmission coefficient.

Transition state theory, together with thermodynamics, thus enables us to calculate equilibrium and reaction rates from the appropriate potential energy surfaces, or conversely, to deduce properties of the potential surface in configuration space from observed rates and equilibria.

It may be useful to outline how rates and equilibria reflect the various properties of the potential energy surface. From the height, the curvatures, and the absolute configuration of a potential minimum, one can calculate the thermodynamic properties of the species represented by the minimum, and if these properties are known for two minima, the corresponding equilibrium constant can be calculated. Whenever these properties are known for a saddlepoint and a potential minimum, the corresponding reaction rate can be calculated. Conversely, when rates and equilibrium are measured for enough temperatures, concentrations, and isotopes, the properties of the potential surface can be deduced. If the same reactants can react by passing over two competitive barriers to yield two sets of products, kT times the logarithm of the ratio of the two rates gives the difference in free energy of the two barriers at their transition states. If the temperature coefficient of this free energy is measured, the difference in height of the two barriers can be determined. The change in the transmission coefficient, κ, with different isotopic compositions, reflects the change in zero point energies, the barrier curvatures, and the leakage through the barrier.

Irradiation of reactants or the bombarding of them with electrons corresponds to jumping vertically to a higher potential surface in configuration space. The system may then have enough energy to break up by passing over a potential barrier on the upper surface; or where surfaces cross each other, the system may roll through the crossing region down to a lower surface thus converting the absorbed energy into heat.

It is difficult to think of a more rewarding way of interpreting a complicated sequence of reactions than to draw the relevant parts of the associated potential surfaces in configuration space and then from these to deduce the course that the reactions should take.

Readings and References

Brown, D. E., Johnson, F. H., and Marsland, D. A., "The Pressure-Temperature Relations of Bacterial Luminescence," *J. Cellular Comp. Physiol.,* **20,** 151–168 (1942).

Chase, A. M., and Langridge, R., "The Sedimentation Constant and Molecular Weight of Cypridina Luciferase," *Arch. Biochem. Biophys.,* **88,** 294–297 (1960).

Ehrlich, G., "Low-Temperature Chemisorption: I. Flash Desorption of Nitrogen," *J. Chem. Phys.,* **34,** 29–38 (1961).

Eyring, H., and Magee, J. L., "Application of the theory of absolute reaction rates to bacterial luminescence," *J. Cellular Comp. Physiol.,* **20,** 169–177 (1942).

Heideger, W. J., and Boudart, M., "Interfacial Resistance to Evaporation," *Chem. Eng. Sci.,* **17,** 1–10 (1962).

Johnson, F. H., Eyring, H., and Polissar, M. J., "The Kinetic Basis of Molecular Biology," John Wiley & Sons, Inc., New York, 1954.

Johnson, F. H., Eyring, H., Steblay, R., Chaplin, H., Huber, C., and Gheradi, G., "The Nature and Control of Reactions in Bio-luminescence," *J. Gen. Physiol.,* **28,** 463–537 (1945).

Johnson, F. H., and Flagler, E. A., "Hydrostatic Pressure Reversal of Narcosis in Tadpoles," *Science,* **112,** 91–92 (1951).

Johnson, F. H., Sie, E. H.-C., and Haneda, Y., "The Luciferin-Luciferase Reaction," in "Light and Life," McElroy, W. D., and Glass, B., eds., The Johns Hopkins Press, Baltimore, 1961, pp. 206–217.

Kincaid, J. F., and Eyring, H., "Free Volumes and Free Angle Ratios of Molecules in Liquids," *J. Chem. Phys.,* **6,** 620–629 (1938).

Mortensen, E. M., and Eyring, H., "Transmission Coefficients for Evaporation and Condensation," *J. Phys. Chem.,* **64,** 846–849 (1960).

Ree, T. S., Ree, T., Eyring, H., and Fueno, T., "Activated Complexes of Fast Biomolecular Reactions," *J. Chem. Phys.,* **36,** 281–286 (1962).

Wanlass, F. M., "Gas-Solid Interactions," Ph.D. Thesis, University of Utah, 1962.

Wyllie, G., "Evaporation and Surface Structure of Liquids," *Proc. Roy. Soc. (London),* **A 197,** 383–395 (1949).

chapter six ─────────────────────────────

RAPID REACTIONS IN
AQUEOUS SOLUTIONS

THE EXPERIMENTS customarily used in an undergraduate physical chemistry laboratory to illustrate problems in chemical kinetics deal with reactions in aqueous solution having very low specific rates. The student never catches a glimpse of one of the most important experimental frontiers in present-day chemical kinetics: the measurement of rates of very rapid reactions in solution. (Happily, this little book lies outside the domain of the FCC, so we need not give equal time to recent, exciting developments in the study of fast gaseous reactions by flash photolytic, shock tube, and mass spectrometric techniques.) Once we have introduced the general subject of rapid reactions in solutions, we will confine our attention, in the interests of clarity, to a few representative methods of studying such reactions.

How Fast is Fast?

Let us illustrate what we mean by rapid reactions in aqueous solutions with the equilibrium

$$H^+ + OH^- \underset{k_D}{\overset{k_R}{\rightleftharpoons}} H_2O \qquad 6.1$$

Hereafter, it will be tacitly assumed that the proton in such an equilibrium is solvated. Using the dissociation field effect method, a relaxation technique that we will describe shortly, Eigen and De Maeyer (1955) measured $k_R = (1.4 \pm 0.2) \times 10^{11}$ M^{-1} sec^{-1} for this reaction. (M^{-1} sec^{-1} is an abbreviation for liters $mole^{-1}$ sec^{-1}.) From the dissociation constant $K = [H^+][OH^-]/[H_2O] = k_D/k_R = 1.821_4 \times 10^{-16}$ M at $25°$ C it follows that $k_D = 2.5 \times 10^{-5}$ sec^{-1}. The above value of k_R is the highest specific rate reliably determined in aqueous solutions. Hereafter, the expression "rapid reaction" will describe any bimolecular process having a specific rate in the range of ~ 10 to 10^{11} M^{-1} sec^{-1}. There is good reason to believe that specific rates in excess of 2×10^{11} M^{-1} sec^{-1} for reactions in aqueous solution are spurious. The lower limit to the range of "rapid reactions" is arbitrary; a specific rate of 10 M^{-1} sec^{-1} is the approximate maximum accessible to study by classical methods. For instance, Asknes and Prue (1959) were able to measure with conventional titration techniques the rate of alkaline hydrolysis in aqueous solution ($25°$ C) of 3-acetoxypropyl-trimethylammonium iodide

$$(CH_3)_3N^+(CH_2)_3O\overset{\overset{\displaystyle O}{\|}}{C}CH_3 + H_2O \xrightarrow{\ OH^-\ }$$

$$(CH_3)_3N^+(CH_2)_3O^- + CH_3\overset{\overset{\displaystyle O}{\|}}{C}O^- + 2H^+ \qquad 6.2$$

They reported a specific rate $k_{OH} = 0.67$ M^{-1} sec^{-1} for this process with reaction half lives of the order of a minute for the concentrations chosen. On the other hand, the alkaline hydrolysis of 2-acetoxyethyl-trimethylammonium bromide (acetylcholine bromide) was too fast for precise measurement by the same techniques. The estimated specific rate for this latter reaction was $k_{OH} \approx 1.8$ M^{-1} sec^{-1}. It should be noted in passing that the purpose of this work by Asknes and Prue was the elucidation of kinetic salt effects.

The prejudice against values of k_R in water in excess of 2×10^{11} M^{-1} sec^{-1} demands some justification. Debye (1942) assumed that Stokes' law for viscous drag on a macroscopic sphere traveling through a liquid can be applied to ions and derived the following theoretical expression for the maximum specific rate of diffusion-controlled ion recombination in very dilute solutions:

$$k_R \approx \frac{4\pi N Z_1 Z_2 e_0^2 (D_1 + D_2)}{10^3 \epsilon k T \left[\exp\left(\dfrac{Z_1 Z_2 e_0^2}{\epsilon k T \sigma} \right) - 1 \right]} \qquad 6.3$$

The symbols have the following meanings: $N = 6.02 \times 10^{23}$ molecules mole^{-1}, $Z_1 =$ the valence (either a positive or negative integer) of ion 1, $e_0 = 4.80 \times 10^{-10}$ statcoulombs (often denoted just esu), $D_1 =$ diffusion coefficient of ion 1 in cm^2 sec^{-1}, $\epsilon =$ dimensionless dielectric constant, $k = 1.38 \times 10^{-16}$ erg deg^{-1}, $T =$ Kelvin temperature, and σ is an effective-reaction distance in cm. With the various quantities expressed in these units the maximum specific rate will be in M^{-1} sec^{-1}. Eigen and De Maeyer (1958) have shown that for most ion recombinations in very dilute aqueous solution the reaction distance $\sigma \approx 7.5$ Å. At this interionic distance it is reasonable to use the macroscopic dielectric constant of water ($\epsilon = 78.5$ at 298° K) in Eq. 6.3. Tabulations of ionic mobilities u_i (more properly "electrical mobility," the velocity attained by the ion under unit potential gradient) are more common than are tables of ionic diffusion coefficients. The two quantities for a given ion are related by Nernst's equation

$$u_i = \frac{|Z_i| e_0 D_i}{kT} \qquad 6.4$$

The convention is to express the ion mobility u_i in the mongrel units cm^2 volt^{-1} sec^{-1}. Therefore taking $e_0 = 1.60 \times 10^{-19}$ coulombs, $k = 1.38 \times 10^{-23}$ joules deg^{-1}, and T in degrees Kelvin, we can readily obtain D_i in cm^2 sec^{-1} from a given value of u_i. In Table 6.1 we give the results of such a calculation for a few interesting cases.

Tables of equivalent ionic conductivity λ_i, in cm^2 ohm^{-1} equiv^{-1}, are also readily available. The ionic mobility can be calculated from such information using the relation $\lambda_i = Fu_i$, where F is Faraday's constant $= 96,500$ coulombs equiv^{-1}.

The ion with the highest mobility in water is H_3O^+. The second highest ionic mobility in water is that of OH^-. All other ions in aqueous solution have much lower and roughly equal mobilities. Equation 6.3 takes no account of steric factors, but since the reaction between H_3O^+ and OH^- has a steric factor of unity anyway, we would naturally expect this to be the fastest ion recombination reaction occurring in aqueous systems. Substituting all the appropriate numerical values except diffusion coefficients in Eq. 6.3, we have for the maximum k_R of oppositely charged monovalent ions in water at 25° C:

$$k_R \approx 8.80 \times 10^{14}(D_1 + D_2) \qquad 6.5$$

Inserting $D_{H_3O^+}$ and D_{OH^-} from Table 6.1, we calculate a maximum $k_R = 1.3 \times 10^{11}$ M^{-1} sec^{-1} in good agreement

TABLE 6.1. Experimental Ion Mobilities u_i in Water at 25° C and Corresponding Ion Diffusion Coefficients D_i Calculated from Eq. 6.4

Ion	H_3O^+	NH_4^+	OH^-	F^-	OAc^-
$u_i(10^{-4}$ cm^2 volt^{-1} sec^{-1})	36.2	7.6	19.8	5.6	4.2
$D_i(10^{-5}$ cm^2 sec^{-1})	9.28	1.9	5.08	1.4	1.1

with the experimental value $(1.4 \pm 0.2) \times 10^{11}$ M^{-1} sec^{-1} mentioned previously. Of course, the agreement hinges on the choice of the parameter σ. However, the value 7.5 Å gives good agreement not simply for the neutralization of water but also for other systems to be discussed below. Furthermore, the calculated k_R is rather insensitive to the choice of σ within the plausible range between 1 and ~ 12 Å. For instance, for $\sigma = 3$ Å the calculated $k_R = 9 \times 10^{10}$ M^{-1} sec^{-1}.

The argument against values of $k_R > 2 \times 10^{11}$ in water is reinforced by similar results for other simple ionic systems. For instance, the hydrofluoric acid equilibrium

$$H_3O^+ + F^- \underset{k_D}{\overset{k_R}{\rightleftharpoons}} HF + H_2O \qquad 6.6$$

is another in which the steric factor is unity, since the fluoride ion is spherically symmetric. The theoretical maximum k_R is, from Eq. 6.5 and Table 6.1, just 9.4×10^{10} M^{-1} sec^{-1}. The experimental $k_R \sim 1.0 \times 10^{11}$ M^{-1} sec^{-1} was measured by Eigen and Kustin (1960) by the use of the dissociation field effect method. The essence of this relaxation method (Eigen and Schoen, 1955) is the perturbation of a $\sim 10^{-4}$ M ionic strength, weak acid equilibrium by the sudden application across a sophisticated Wheatstone bridge of an electric field having a field density of the order of 10^5 volt cm^{-1}.

Now all electrolytes whether completely or incompletely dissociated (strong or weak) experience the so-called First Wien Effect. For instance, a sodium ion in an NaCl solution will be so strongly accelerated toward the cathode by a high field density that the Na^+ will be pulled right out from under its Debye-Huckel atmosphere of chloride ions and will move so rapidly through solution that there will be insufficient time for such a cloud of countercharges to re-form around it.

The result is a 1% to 2% increase in ionic conductance above that anticipated by Ohm's law.

In the dissociation field effect technique this increase in conductance is cancelled by placing a solution of a strong electrolyte such as HCl in the reference arm of the Wheatstone bridge. The dissociation field effect or Second Wien Effect that is observed is characteristic only of weak electrolytes such as acetic acid placed in the sample arm of the bridge. The electric field displaces the weak acid equilibrium

$$HA \rightleftharpoons H^+ \cdots A^- \rightleftharpoons H^+ + A^- \qquad 6.7$$

to the right producing a non-Ohmic conductance increase of the order of 10% at 10^5 volt/cm, depending on concentration. In effect, the suddenly applied field takes hold of many ion pairs $H^+ \ldots A^-$ and pulls them apart. Since the concentration of ion pairs is comparatively low, the result is a dissociation of some HA all the way to the completely separate ions H^+ and A^-. The increase in conductance is measured on an oscilloscope as an imbalance of the Wheatstone bridge. Using electric field pulses of varying lengths but of the order of the half time (10^{-7} sec) of the ion recombination (relaxation) process, one can calculate a k_R from the dispersion of the amplitude of the conductance change and the known ion concentrations and equilibrium constant. Some representative results obtained by this method are shown in Table 6.2.

Steric factors for the recombinations involving the structurally more complicated anions lower the specific rates perceptibly though never by as much as a factor of 10. In general, we may say that the rate constant of a diffusion-controlled protolytic reaction will lie in the range 10^{10} to 10^{11} M^{-1} sec^{-1} unless both recombining ions have the same charge sign, in which case a lower specific rate is possible. With this

TABLE 6.2. Specific Rates of Ion Recombination Obtained by the Dissociation Field Effect Method

Ions	Experimental k_R (M^{-1} sec^{-1})	
$H_3O^+ + CH_3COO^-$	4.5×10^{10}	(Eigen and Schoen, 1955)
$NH_4^+ + OH^-$	3×10^{10}	
$H_3O^+ + HS^-$	7.5×10^{10}	(Eigen and Kustin, 1960)
$H_3O^+ + O_2NC_6H_4O^-$ (*p*-nitrophenol)	3.6×10^{10}	
$H_3O^+ + H_2NC_6H_4COO^-$ (*p*-aminobenzoic acid)	3.7×10^{10}	(Eigen and Eyring, 1962)
$H_3O^+ + C_8H_{11}N_2O_3^-$ (barbital)	4.2×10^{10}	

fact clearly established, the most profitable future application of the dissociation field effect method will probably be to nonaqueous systems.

Flow Methods

Many techniques have been developed recently that make the study of rapid reactions in aqueous solution possible. Flow techniques, first developed by Roughton and Hartridge (1923), allow one to measure reaction half times in the range between 10 sec and 10^{-3} sec. Let us see how large a specific rate of a second order reaction we can determine with this lowest measurable value of the half time $t_{1/2}$. Integrating the rate expression $dx/dt = k_2(a - x)(b - x)$, we have

$$\frac{1}{a - b} \ln \frac{b(a - x)}{a(b - x)} = k_2 t \qquad 6.8$$

Assuming that the initial concentrations of the reactants are $a = 5 \times 10^{-3}$ M and $b = 5 \times 10^{-5}$ M, we may substitute these values of a and b plus $t = 10^{-3}$ sec and $x = b/2$ in Eq. 6.8 and obtain $k_2 = 1.4 \times 10^5$ M^{-1} sec^{-1}. The measurement of shorter half reaction times by this method is complicated by problems of incomplete mixing of reactants and cavitation (bubble formation) at high flow rates.

Competition Methods

It is possible to measure shorter half reaction times in either one of two ways. The reaction can be forced to compete with a physical process having a known time constant, or the equilibrium can be subjected to a fast perturbation and the equilibration process can be measured directly. The polarographic method is the oldest of the competition methods; the competition in this case is between the formation of a reducible ion and its diffusion to the cathode (Brdička, 1960; Koryta, 1960). The polarographic method has produced the bulk of the presently available information concerning rates of electron transfer between transition metal complexes in aqueous solutions (Halpern, 1961). The fastest such reactions have specific rates in the neighborhood of 10^6 M^{-1} sec^{-1}. However, the polarograph is a less satisfactory tool for measuring specific rates of diffusion controlled protolytic reactions, since the values of k_R obtained are often improbably large (Brdička, 1960; Strehlow, 1960).

Nuclear magnetic resonance spectrometry (Purcell and Bloch, 1946) provides another competition method for following fast-exchange reactions in liquids. For simplicity, we will confine this discussion to proton magnetic resonance. There are, for instance, two ways that protons occur in methanol: (1) where there is one proton in the hydroxyl groups and (2) where there are three of a kind in the methyl group.

The diamagnetic screening of the external magnetic field by the electrons surrounding a proton gives rise to a distinctive magnetic environment for each of these two types of protons in the methanol molecule. As a consequence, the nuclear-spin transitions of the two kinds of protons occur at different magnetic field strengths. The separation of the two absorption lines in the resulting spectrum is called the "chemical shift." Actually, neither line is simple. The various possible combinations of the nuclear spin of the hydroxyl proton with the nuclear spins of the three methyl group protons give rise to splitting of the two major resonance lines as shown in Fig. 6.1. This splitting due to magnetic interaction between nonequivalent protons in the same molecule is called indirect spin-spin interaction. The four hydroxyl resonance lines correspond to the four possible spin states of the methyl protons (↑↑↑, ↑↑↓, ↑↓↓, ↓↓↓).

The rate of exchange of hydroxyl protons between methanol molecules in very concentrated aqueous solutions (2% to 4% water by weight) is accelerated by acidic or basic conditions. At low rates of exchange in neutral solutions the methyl proton doublet and hydroxyl proton quadruplet are fairly well defined though not as sharp as in the theoretical curve of Fig. 6.1 because of exchange broadening at even the lowest exchange rates attainable. Unless the system is anhydrous, a water line will also appear as a shoulder on the high field side of the hydroxyl resonance, that is, the chemical shift between hydroxyl and water protons is much less than that between hydroxyl and methyl protons.

As the rate of proton exchange is increased by the addition

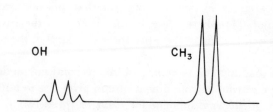

Fig. 6.1. Theoretical NMR spectrum of methyl alcohol. Magnetic field increases from left to right.

of acid (HCl) or base (sodium methoxide), all the peaks broaden. This increase in peak width due to exchange can be interpreted in terms of the mean lifetime τ of a proton between successive exchanges. The peak width is proportional to the reciprocal of τ. As this time τ between exchanges becomes shorter, the nuclear spin state of the proton becomes less and less well defined. With increasing exchange rate, the two peaks of the methyl doublet broaden, decrease in height, and begin to overlap. Both methyl lines almost melt into the baseline when τ equals the reciprocal of their spin-spin splitting in cycles per second. This first stage of broadened individual lines can be called "lifetime broadening," since it results from the decreasing finite time a nucleus stays in a definite spin state.

For higher rates of exchange the protons "remember" at least partially their spin state in their previous environment and the two peaks of the doublet coalesce to form a single peak of increasing height and narrowness, that is, at sufficiently rapid rates of exchange the hydroxyl protons have a single average spin state with exchange causing only small, random fluctuations from this average. The hydroxyl quadruplet changes simultaneously in an analogous fashion. Either multiplet therefore gives an independent determination of the hydroxyl proton exchange rate. One of several processes occurring in this system for which Meiboom *et al.* (1959) measured a specific rate is Eq. 6.9, where the experimental

$$CH_3OH + CH_3O^- \overset{k_2}{\rightleftharpoons} CH_3O^- + CH_3OH \qquad 6.9$$

$k_2 = 9.3 \times 10^6$ M^{-1} sec^{-1} at 22° C in a nearly anyhdrous basic system. It should now be clearer why this NMR technique is classified as a competition method. It is possible to observe transformations between the proton spin resonance lines of two chemical states only if the transformation (exchange) frequency is slow compared to the frequency difference of the two lines (spin-spin splitting).

The results obtained with methanol illustrate the unique capability of the NMR method to measure protolytic reaction rates involving exchange between identical particles. Another interesting illustration concerns the anomalously high mobility of H_3O^+ and OH^- in aqueous solution that we mentioned earlier. These high mobilities are due to the occurrence of fast proton transfers between these ions and neutral water molecules (Eigen and De Maeyer, 1958):

$$H_2O + H_3O^+ \xrightarrow{k_1} H_2\overset{+}{O}H + H_2O \qquad 6.10$$

$$OH_2 + \overset{-}{O}H \xrightarrow{k_2} \overset{-}{O}H + HOH \qquad 6.11$$

The rate-determining step of these reactions is the required re-orientation of the water molecules between successive proton exchanges. Apparently, this involves the migration of very strong hydrogen bonds ("structural diffusion") in an $H_9O_4^+$ complex rather than a rotation of individual H_3O^+ units in space. Using NMR exchange broadening techniques, Meiboom (1961) found that

$$k_1 = (10.6 \pm 4)10^9 \text{ M}^{-1} \text{ sec}^{-1} \qquad 6.12$$

and

$$k_2 = (3.8 \pm 1.5)10^9 \text{ M}^{-1} \text{ sec}^{-1} \qquad 6.13$$

As one might expect, it is also possible to study proton exchange rates between chemically nonidentical species by measuring proton line broadening where the lines are separated by a chemical shift. For instance, Pearson *et al.* (1960) measured $k_2 = 3.8 \times 10^6$ M^{-1} sec^{-1} at 25° C for the process

$$Cr - NH + OH^- \xrightarrow{k_2} Cr - N^- + H_2O \qquad 6.14$$

in a basic 0.01 M aqueous solution of Cr (ethylenediamine)$_3$ (ClO$_4$)$_3$. Since there are other experimental methods of studying fast exchange reactions between different chemical species, this application is less important than the methanol or water studies described above. The only significant limitation of the NMR-line-broadening method of studying exchange kinetics is a rather narrow-reaction-half-life time range of about 1 sec to 10^{-3} sec.

Perturbation Methods

A number of perturbation methods of studying rapid reactions in solutions have been developed since 1950. Though first used by Porter (1950) to study gaseous reactions, the flash photolysis method is now widely used in investigating reactions in solution. A short, very intense flash of light is used to drastically perturb the equilibrium between solute ground and excited electronic states or free radicals. The return to equilibrium after the flash, with attendant reversion of products to reactants, can be followed by the employing of ultraviolet and visible absorption spectroscopy but with a second light beam that is much less intense than the beam responsible for the photolysis. The limiting factor in studying fast reactions by this method is the finite duration of the photolysis flash; a flash of sufficient intensity falls to half its peak intensity in not less than 2 to 10 microsec, and shorter chemical half reaction times cannot be investigated. However, at least in principle, the choice of suitable concentrations brings the fastest diffusion-controlled second order reactions in aqueous solutions within the range of this technique. It is also possible to determine first order rate constants as large as 10^5 sec^{-1}.

There are several new perturbation techniques, including the dissociation field effect method mentioned earlier, that are classified as "relaxation methods" (Eigen, 1954). The "temperature-jump" (Czerlinski and Eigen, 1959) "pressure-jump" (Ljunggren and Lamm, 1958; Strehlow and Becker, 1959) and the semiclassical ultrasonic absorption techniques (Tamm, 1960) all belong to this category. The ultrasonic wave absorption technique is used to study rates and mechanism of fast intramolecular processes such as proton transfer between the carboxyl and amino groups in the aminobenzoic acids. The other relaxation methods have been used to study redox, acid-base, and ligand equilibria as well as tautomeric transformations and enzyme catalysis.

In all relaxation methods a chemical equilibrium is perturbed by a rapid change in one of several possible external parameters (electric field intensity, temperature, or pressure), and the equilibration process is then followed by spectrophotometric or conductometric techniques. Changes in the solvent structure effected by this same perturbation proceed so much faster than the chemical reactions under investigation that they are unobservable within the time range accessible to the relaxation methods and cause no ambiguity in the experimental results. A broad spectrum of reaction half lives ranging from a few seconds down to 5×10^{-10} sec have been measured with these methods, although no one of the methods covers this entire time range. A broad range of accessible times is important when the reaction mechanism is unknown and more than one fast reaction step must be detected.

The interpretation of a spectrum of measured relaxation times in a single chemical system requires an elaborate mathematical analysis (Eigen, 1954, 1960) that must take into consideration the nature of the perturbation (De Maeyer, 1960). In the interests of clarity we will consider a single-step chemical process

$$AB \underset{k_R}{\overset{k_D}{\rightleftharpoons}} A^+ + B^- \qquad 6.15$$

but we remind the reader that the much more common multistep chemical processes can be handled with comparable ease by the same general techniques. The rate equation for the above equilibrium is

$$\frac{dx}{dt} = k_D(a - x) - k_R x^2 \qquad 6.16$$

where a is the total concentration of AB and x is the concentration of A^+ or B^-. Now let $\Delta x \equiv x - x_e$ where x_e is the ionic concentration at equilibrium and Δx is small. This restriction to small perturbations is important, since we wish for mathematical simplicity to deal only with linear differential equations. Since x_e is a constant, it necessarily follows that $dx_e/dt = 0$. Substituting $x = \Delta x + x_e$ in Eq. 6.16, rearranging terms and neglecting the product $k_R \Delta x^2$, we then have

$$\frac{d\Delta x}{dt} = -(k_D + 2k_R x_e)\Delta x + k_D(a - x_e) - k_R x_e^2 \qquad 6.17$$

From Eq. 6.16 and the fact that x_e is a constant, we see that

$$\frac{dx_e}{dt} = 0 = k_D(a - x_e) - k_R x_e^2 \qquad 6.18$$

Eq. 6.17 therefore reduces to

$$\frac{d\Delta x}{dt} = -(k_D + 2k_R x_e)\Delta x \qquad 6.19$$

The casual observer might raise the objection that an interest in $d\Delta x/dt$ seems scarcely justified when we have imposed the condition that $dx/dt \approx 0$ (small perturbations). However, the linear motion in space of a Newtonian mass point provides a familiar analogy. Such a mass point with zero initial velocity can be brought into motion by a very large linear acceleration. Equation 6.19 is interesting because the parenthesized quantity on the right has the dimensions of reciprocal time.

Thus we may rewrite 6.19 as

$$\frac{d\Delta x}{dt} = -\frac{\Delta x}{\tau} \qquad 6.20$$

where the "relaxation time" τ is given by

$$\tau \equiv (k_D + 2k_R x_e)^{-1} \qquad 6.21$$

This time is not to be identified with any specific, simple physical (chemical) process taking place in the liquid. In the case of the temperature-jump method where to a first approximation the perturbation is a square step function (a 10° C jump in temperature in less than a microsecond) it is easy to evaluate τ because of the obvious logarithmic character of Eq. 6.20. All that is required is a measurement following perturbation of the time dependence of the concentration of one of the reacting species (or that of a coupled species). τ will be the time in which this concentration drops to $1/e$ of its initial value. If the equilibrium constant is unkown but $k_D \approx 2k_R x_e$, it is possible to determine both k_D and k_R by varying concentrations. If the equilibrium constant $K = k_D/k_R$ is known, it is easy to evaluate both k_R and k_D since Eq. 6.21 is readily transformed into

$$k_R = [\tau([A^+] + [B^-] + K)]^{-1} \qquad 6.22$$

The symbols $[A^+]$ and $[B^-]$ denote ionic concentrations that will generally be known from the preparation of the sample solution. Equation 6.22 is more widely applicable than one would suppose from Eq. 6.21; $[A^+]$ and $[B^-]$ can differ in magnitude by a factor of 10^2 and Eq. 6.22 will still yield reliable results.

Temperature-Jump Method

We will conclude this chapter with a description of the mechanics of the temperature-jump method, perhaps the most versatile of the relaxation techniques. A simplified schematic is shown in Fig. 6.2. The 30 kv voltage generator charges the 0.1 microfarad condenser C to the voltage at which the spark gap G breaks down. The condenser then discharges across G and through the sample cell S, containing an aqueous 0.1 M ionic strength solution, to ground. S is a ~50 ml plexiglass cell containing two platinum electrodes spaced 1 cm apart and immersed in an aqueous 0.1 M ionic strength solution. The sudden surge of current raises the temperature of the 1 ml volume of solution between the electrodes by 10° C in a few microseconds. If we make the rough approximation that none of the energy stored in the condenser is dissipated in the spark gap, we can estimate the magnitude of the temperature-jump from

$$E = \tfrac{1}{2}CV^2 = \tfrac{1}{2}(10^{-7} \text{ farads})(3 \times 10^4 \text{ volts})^2 = 45 \text{ watt sec} \qquad 6.23$$

and

$$\Delta T \approx \frac{E}{C_p \rho V} = 10° \text{ C} \qquad 6.24$$

where C_p is the heat capacity (approximately that of water), ρ is the liquid density (also that of H_2O) and $V \cong 1$ ml. The cell design is such that the new, higher temperature (usually

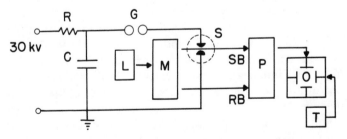

Fig. 6.2. Simplified schematic of a temperature-jump apparatus.

25° C) persists in this 1 ml volume for a long time compared to the fast chemical relaxation times being measured.

Now let us first consider what happens when we jump the temperature of an aqueous solution that is 10^{-5} M in phenolphthalein, 10^{-5} M in OH^- (by adding KOH) and 10^{-1} M in KNO_3. The monochromator, M, is adjusted to pass only $\sim$552 millimicron light from the lamp, L. This wavelength when absorbed from white light by the anion In^{-2} or more precisely

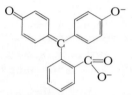

of the phenolphthalein equilibrium

$$H_2In + 2OH^- \rightleftharpoons In^{-2} + 2H_2O \qquad 6.25$$

gives rise to the familiar pink color of basic solutions near pH 9. In addition to the sample beam SB that traverses a quartz-sample solution light path through the sample cell there is a reference beam RB that passes through air to the photomultiplier bridge, P. The two beams are compared in intensity at P, and the difference signal is applied to the vertical plates of the oscilloscope, O. With the two light beams initially balanced in intensity, the temperature jump (from 15° to 25° C) is effected, and the oscilloscope horizontal sweep is triggered by the spark discharge at G. The combination of a full, nearly vertical line and the dashed horizontal line in Fig. 6.3 indicates the approximate path of the oscilloscope sweep. Clearly the concentration of In^{-2} ion in the sample cell has precipitously decreased. Several explanations might account for the fact that the curve does not peak at

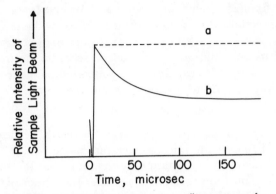

Fig. 6.3. Schematic temperature-jump oscilloscope traces for a) an aqueous 10^{-5} M phenolphthalein- 10^{-1} M KNO$_3$ solution adjusted with KOH to pH 9 and b) a solution with these same concentrations that is also 5.6×10^{-3} M in N,N-dimethyl-o-aminobenzoic acid. An increase in sample beam intensity indicates a decrease in In^{-2} concentration.

$t = 0$, but instead at about 10 microseconds: 1) the heating process is fast but of finite duration, 2) the shift in the phenolphthalein equilibrium possibly has a relaxation time of a few microseconds, or 3) the discharge of the capacitor across the spark gap G causes a strong electromagnetic disturbance of the electronics. The third explanation is correct. The time constant for capacitor discharge through the sample cell is of the order of a microsecond, and the phenolphthalein equilibrium relaxation time is even shorter.

One might well ask why the phenolphthalein equilibrium is perturbed at all. Two broad generalizations regarding the temperature dependence of equilibrium constants are pertinent:

1) Acetic acid is representative of many weak carboxylic acids in that its acid dissociation constant decreases slightly from 1.75×10^{-5} to 1.54×10^{-5} M as the temperature is

raised from 25° to 60° C (Everett and Wynne-Jones, 1939). This is explained by a concurrent decrease in the dielectric constant of water with rising temperature that causes a decrease in the ability of the solvent to separate electrostatic charges (ions). This explanation is supported by the fact that the acid equilibrium constant for the process

$$NH_4^+ + H_2O \rightarrow NH_3 + H_3O^+$$

where no charge separation occurs increases by nearly a factor of 10 over this same temperature range.

2) An equally important observation is that the smaller the acid ionization constant the greater the tendency for K_a to increase with temperature in spite of the difficulties of separating unlike charges. For example, the K_a of water increases from 1.01×10^{-14} at 25° C to 9.62×10^{-14} at 60° C. The explanation of this phenomenon lies in the thermodynamic relation $K = e^{-\frac{\Delta H}{RT}} e^{\frac{\Delta S}{R}}$. A plot of K versus T will be a steeply rising exponential curve with a much greater ΔK for a given increment in T when the acid is weak. Phenolphthalein is quite a weak acid, $K = K_1 K_2 = 10^{-9}$, and its dissociation constant increases by a factor of about 3 as temperature rises from 18° to 70° C (Kolthoff, 1921). Now K for equilibrium (6.25) above is $K = K_1 K_2 / K_w^2$, and we would expect on the basis of the foregoing information that this quotient would decrease with rising temperature, since the increase in K_w with temperature exceeds that of $K_1 K_2$. This agrees nicely with the experimental result of Fig. 6.3.

If the sample solution is also 5.6×10^{-3} M in N,N-dimethyl-o-aminobenzoic acid for which the experimental second acid ionization constant is $K_2 = 3.8 \times 10^{-9}$ M at 0.1 M ionic strength, we must consider in addition to 6.25 the equilibrium

$$R + OH^- \underset{k_D}{\overset{k_R}{\rightleftharpoons}} R^- + H_2O \qquad 6.26$$

Since because of rapid intramolecular proton transfer they are indistinguishable by this method, R represents both the neutral molecule of the acid and the corresponding zwitterion (dipolar ion). For Eq. 6.26 the equilibrium constant is $K = k_R/k_D = K_2/K_w$. In the light of the preceding discussion we would expect this equilibrium to be also displaced to the left by a rise in temperature.

We would further expect the specific rate k_R of Eq. 6.26 to be drastically reduced from the diffusion-controlled value of about 10^{10} M^{-1} sec^{-1} by the hydrogen bond stabilization of the zwitterion. The consequent delay in attainment of equilibrium is reflected in the exponential curve b of Fig. 6.3. As before, the In^{-2} concentration decreases sharply as a consequence of the rapid thermal shift in the phenolphthalein equilibrium. However, the more slowly responding N,N-dimethyl-o-aminobenzoic acid equilibrium further pushes up the OH^- concentration with a consequent displacement of the much more dilute phenolphthalein equilibrium back to higher In^{-2} concentrations. From the relaxation time $\tau = 31$ microseconds of the exponential curve and Eq. 6.22 we calculate $k_R = 10^7$ M^{-1} sec^{-1} for the N,N-dimethyl-o-amino-benzoic acid equilibrium (Eigen and Eyring, 1962). This result is particularly intriguing, since at no time have we directly measured changes in concentration of any of the species in the aminobenzoic acid equilibrium.

This elegantly simple example scarcely suggests the diversity of equilibria susceptible to study by the temperature-jump method. One of the most exciting applications presently being pioneered is the investigation of enzyme-catalyzed reactions; many biochemical processes have specific rates within the range of this technique. A wide variety of aqueous, inorganic systems have also been investigated.

Absolute Rate Theory Applied to Fast Reactions

Absolute reaction rate theory provides an instructive treatment of reactions slightly displaced from equilibrium. Consider the reaction

$$A + B \underset{k_b}{\overset{k_f}{\rightleftharpoons}} C + D \qquad 6.27$$

Let (A), (B), (C) and (D) represent the initial equilibrium concentration and $(A - x)$, $(B - x)$, $(C + x)$ and $(D + x)$ the concentrations after time t. Consider as an example what happens as the temperature is jumped from T_1 to $T_1 + \Delta T$. Initially, forward and backward reactions balance. Thus

$$k_{fT_1}(A)(B) - k_{bT_1}(C)(D) = 0 \qquad 6.28$$

If the temperature is jumped to

$$T_2 = T_1 + \Delta T \qquad 6.29$$

the rate of reaction obeys the equation:

$$\frac{dx}{dt} = k_{fT_2}(A - x)(B - x) - k_{bT_2}(C + x)(D + x) \qquad 6.30$$

Here the T subscripts indicate the temperature of reaction. The specific rate constants can be represented in general as

$$k_{fT_1} = T_1{}^m L e^{-\frac{\Delta H^{\ddagger}}{RT_1}} \qquad 6.31$$

where L is the temperature independent factor. It will be convenient to consider the very common case where $m = 1$.

This includes ordinary reactions where the limiting rate is the passage over a single barrier as well as diffusion where the process involves passage over a succession of barriers of equal height. In this latter case the temperature independent term will contain other factors than $e^{\frac{\Delta S^{\ddagger}}{R}}$ but temperature independent factors do not effect our analysis of the temperature jump.

Thus consider

$$k_{fT_1} = \kappa \frac{kT_1}{h} e^{-\frac{\Delta F_f^{\ddagger}}{RT_1}} = \kappa \frac{kT_1}{h} e^{\frac{\Delta S_f^{\ddagger}}{R}} e^{-\frac{\Delta H_f^{\ddagger}}{RT_1}} \qquad 6.32$$

and

$$k_{fT_2} = \kappa \frac{k(T_1 + \Delta T)}{h} e^{-\frac{\Delta F_f^{\ddagger}}{RT_1\left(1 + \frac{\Delta T}{T_1}\right)}}$$

$$= \kappa \frac{kT_1}{h} \left(1 + \frac{\Delta T}{T_1}\right) e^{\frac{\Delta S_f^{\ddagger}}{R}} e^{-\frac{\Delta H_f^{\ddagger}}{RT_1\left(1 + \frac{\Delta T}{T_1}\right)}} \qquad 6.33$$

A further expansion of k_{fT_2} gives

$$k_{fT_2} \approx \kappa \frac{kT_1}{h} \left(1 + \frac{\Delta T}{T_1}\right) e^{\frac{\Delta S_f^{\ddagger}}{R}} e^{-\frac{\Delta H_f^{\ddagger}\left(1 - \frac{\Delta T}{T_1}\right)}{RT_1}}$$

$$= \kappa \frac{kT_1}{h} e^{\frac{\Delta S_f^{\ddagger}}{R}} e^{-\frac{\Delta H_f^{\ddagger}}{RT_1}} e^{\frac{\Delta H_f^{\ddagger}\Delta T}{RT_1^2}} \left(1 + \frac{\Delta T}{T_1}\right)$$

$$= k_{fT_1} e^{\frac{\Delta H_f^{\ddagger}\Delta T}{RT_1^2}} \left(1 + \frac{\Delta T}{T_1}\right) \qquad 6.34$$

Substituting Eq. 6.34 as well as the analogous result for k_{bT_2} and also Eq. 6.28 into Eq. 6.30 yields

$$\frac{dx}{dt} = k_{fT_1}(A)(B)\left(1 + \frac{\Delta T}{T_1}\right)\Bigg\{ e^{\frac{\Delta H_f^{\ddagger}\Delta T}{RT_1^2}}\left(1 - \frac{x}{(A)}\right)$$

$$\left(1 - \frac{x}{(B)}\right) - e^{\frac{\Delta H_b^{\ddagger}\Delta T}{RT_1^2}}\left(1 + \frac{x}{(C)}\right)\left(1 + \frac{x}{(D)}\right)\Bigg\} \quad 6.35$$

For very fast reactions for which

$$\frac{\Delta H_f^{\ddagger}\Delta T}{RT_1^2} \ll 1 \qquad\qquad 6.36$$

Eq. 6.35 may be expanded as follows neglecting small terms:

$$\frac{dx}{dt} = k_{fT_1}(A)(B)\left(1 + \frac{\Delta T}{T_1}\right)\Bigg\{\left(1 + \frac{\Delta H_f^{\ddagger}\Delta T}{RT_1^2}\right)\left(1 - \frac{x}{(A)}\right)\left(1 - \frac{x}{(B)}\right)$$

$$-\left(1 + \frac{\Delta H_b^{\ddagger}\Delta T}{RT_1^2}\right)\left(1 + \frac{x}{(C)}\right)\left(1 + \frac{x}{(D)}\right)\Bigg\} \qquad 6.37$$

or

$$\frac{dx}{dt} = k_{fT_1}(A)(B)\left(1 + \frac{\Delta T}{T_1}\right)\Bigg\{\frac{\Delta H\Delta T}{RT_1^2}$$

$$- x\left(\frac{1}{(A)} + \frac{1}{(B)} + \frac{1}{(C)} + \frac{1}{(D)}\right)\Bigg\} \quad 6.38$$

In deriving Eq. 6.38 from Eq. 6.37 we have used the obvious relationship

$$\Delta H = \Delta H_f^{\ddagger} - \Delta H_b^{\ddagger}$$

Eq. 6.38 can be written in the form

$$\frac{dx}{dt} = k(a - bx) \qquad\qquad 6.39$$

$$\left(-\frac{1}{b}\right)\frac{-b\,dx}{(a - bx)} = k\,dt \qquad\qquad 6.40$$

$$-\frac{1}{b}\ln(a - bx) + c = kt \qquad\qquad 6.41$$

Evaluating the integration constant c so that $t = 0$ when $x = 0$ gives:

$$-\frac{1}{b} \ln\left(\frac{a - bx}{a}\right) = kt \qquad 6.42$$

$$1 - \frac{b}{a}x = e^{-bkt} \qquad 6.43$$

Thus Eq. 6.39 finally brings us to the relationship:

$$x = \frac{a}{b}(1 - e^{-bkt}) \qquad 6.44$$

If k_{fT_1} takes the more general form of Eq. 6.31 with m different from unity, the only effect this has on Eq. 6.38 is to replace the factor $\left(1 + \frac{\Delta T}{T_1}\right)$ by $\left(1 + \frac{\Delta T}{T_1}\right)^m$. Thus we have a useful integrated form for the dependence of concentration on the time for all systems displaced from equilibrium by a temperature jump. Fast reactions are clearly an exciting and challenging new field for present-day reaction kineticists.

Readings and References

Asknes, G., and Prue, J. E., "Kinetic Salt Effects and Mechanism in the Hydrolysis of Positively Charged Esters," *J. Chem. Soc.,* **1959,** 103.

Bloch, F., Hansen, W. W., and Packard, M., "Nuclear Induction," *Phys. Rev.,* **69,** 127 (1946).

Brdička, R., "Schnelle Lösungsreaktionen in den polarographischen Depolarisationsvorgangen und ihre Geschwindigkeitsbestimmung," *Z. Elektrochem.,* **64,** 16 (1960).

Czerlinski, G., and Eigen, M., "Eine Temperatursprungmethode zur Untersuchung chemischer Relaxation," *Z. Elektrochem.,* **63,** 652 (1959).

Debye, P., "Reaction Rates in Ionic Solutions," *Trans. Electrochem. Soc.,* **82,** 265 (1942).

De Maeyer, L., "Methoden zur Untersuchung chemischer Relaxation," *Z. Elektrochem.,* **64,** 65 (1960).

Eigen, M., "Methods for Investigation of Ionic Reactions in Aqueous Solutions with Half-Times as Short as 10^{-9} Sec," *Disc. Faraday Soc.,* **17,** 194 (1954).

Eigen, M., "Relaxationsspektren chemischer Umwandlungen," *Z. Elektrochem.,* **64,** 115 (1960).

Eigen, M., and De Maeyer, L., "Relaxation Methods," in "Investigation of Rates and Mechanisms of Reactions," 2nd ed., vol. 8, part 2, of "Technique of Organic Chemistry," A. Weissberger, ed., chap. 18, Interscience, New York, 1963.

Eigen, M., and De Maeyer, L., "Self-Dissociation and Protonic Charge Transport in Water and Ice," *Proc. Roy. Soc. (London),* **A247,** 505 (1958).

Eigen, M., and De Maeyer, L., "Untersuchungen uber die Kinetik der Neutralisation," *Z. Elektrochem.,* **59,** 986 (1955).

Eigen, M., and Eyring, E. M., "Fast Protolytic Reactions in Aqueous Solutions of Aminobenzoic Acids," *J. Am. Chem. Soc.,* **84,** 3254 (1962).

Eigen, M., and Johnson, J. S., "Kinetics of Reactions in Solution," *Ann. Rev. Phys. Chem.,* **11,** H. Eyring, ed. (Annual Reviews, Inc., Palo Alto, 1960).

Eigen, M., and Kustin, K., "The Influence of Steric Factors in Fast Protolytic Reactions as Studied With HF, H_2S and Substituted Phenols," *J. Am. Chem. Soc.,* **82,** 5952 (1960).

Eigen, M., and Schoen, J., "Stoss-spannungsverfahren zur Untersuchung sehr schell verlaufender Ionenreaktionen in wasseriger Lösung," *Z. Elektrochem.,* **59,** 483 (1955).

Everett, D. H., and Wynne-Jones, W. F. K., "The Thermodynamics of Acid-Base Equilibria," *Trans. Faraday Soc.,* **35,** 1380 (1939).

Frost, A. A., and Pearson, R. G., "Kinetics and Mechanism," 2nd ed., chap. 11, John Wiley & Sons, Inc., New York, 1961.

Halpern, J., "Mechanisms of Electron Transfer and Related Processes in Solution," *Quarterly Rev.,* **15,** 207 (1961).

Hartridge, H., and Roughton, F. J. W., "Measurements of the Rates of Oxidation and Reduction of Hemoglobin," *Nature,* **111,** 325 (1923).

Kolthoff, I. M., "La sensibilité d'indicateurs colorants à des températures plus élevées que la température ordinaire," *Rec. trav. chim.,* **40,** 775 (1921).

Koryta, J., "Anwendungsmöglichkeiten und Begrenzungen der polarographischen Methode zur Verfolgung schneller chemischer Reaktionen in Lösungen," *Z. Elektrochem.,* **64,** 23 (1960).

Ljunggren, S., and Lamm, O., "A Relaxation Method for the Determination of Moderately Rapid Reaction Rates near Chemical Equilibrium," *Acta Chem. Scand.,* **12,** 1834 (1958).

Luz, Z., Gill, D., and Meiboom, S., "NMR Study of the Protolysis Kinetics in Methanol and Ethanol," *J. Chem. Phys.,* **30,** 1540 (1959).

Meiboom, S., "Nuclear Magnetic Resonance Study of the Proton Transfer in Water," *J. Chem. Phys.,* **34,** 375 (1961).

Pearson, R. G., Palmer, J., Anderson, M. M., and Allred, A. L., "Exchange Reactions in Complex Ions by NMR," *Z. Elektrochem.* **64,** 110 (1960).

Porter, G., "Flash Photolysis and Spectroscopy. A New Method for the Study of Free Radical Reactions," *Proc. Roy. Soc. (London),* **A 200,** 284 (1950).

Purcell, E. M., Torrey, H. C., and Pound, R. V., "Resonance Absorption by Nuclear Magnetic Moments in a Solid," *Phys. Rev.,* **69,** 37 (1946).

Strehlow, H., "Fehlerquellen bei der polarographischen Bestimmung der Geschwindigkeitskonstanten schneller chemischer Reaktionen," *Z. Elektrochem.,* **64,** 45 (1960).

Strehlow, H., and Becker, M., "Ein Drucksprung-Verfahren zur Messung der Geschwindigkeit von Ionenreaktionen," *Z. Elektrochem.,* **63,** 457 (1959).

Tamm, K., "Uberblick uber die Verfahren zur Messung der akustischen Relaxation in wässrigen Lösungen," *Z. Elektrochem.,* **64,** 73 (1960).

INDEX